Lelia

First Published 2004 by Countyvise Limited, 14 Appin Road, Birkenhead, Wirral CH41 9HH in association with Liverpool Marine Press.

British Library Cataloguing in Publication Data.
A catalogue record for this book is available from the British Library.

ISBN 1 901231 47 X

Front cover based on a design by Tony Tollitt.

Contents

Acknowledgements

I thank those who have provided me with information: Lelia Sinclair Dickey Baldassari, Steve Brown, Ian Cook, Kevin J Foster, Bob Jones, Richard Harris, Chris Holden, Steve Liscoe, Geoff Oldfield, Roy Rawlinson, Sally Spangler and RDF. I thank the staff of the Liverpool Record Office, the Maritime Museum on Merseyside and the Mariner's Museum, Newport News. I thank Tony Tollitt for help with illustrations. I thank Marilyn for many suggestions for improving my book.

Chris Michael
2004

Chapter 1

14 January 1865

As the boatman pulled them across the Mersey, Thomas Miller could see the *Lelia* more clearly. She had a menacing air. Painted in a drab colour and lying low in the water, she stood out from the other ships. With her long narrow hull and huge paddle wheels she looked built for speed, as indeed she was.

As the boat neared her, Thomas could see on her stern in yellow letters 'Lelia Liverpool'. He felt proud, since Miller & Sons had built her, but also a little anxious since they were responsible for her innovative design which, he hoped, would give her an excellent performance at sea. He was in his late twenties, tall and already taking much of the responsibility for the shipbuilding company founded by his father.

He climbed aboard and was welcomed by her Captain, Thomas Skinner, and by her eventual commander, Arthur Sinclair. Their American accents and Southern hospitality were a noticeable contrast to the Liverpool way of doing things.

Arthur Sinclair was in his fifties, upright, with a distinguished bearing. His appearance confirmed his long experience: 42 years as a naval officer. He had the ruddy complexion of someone who had spent a lifetime at sea, a drooping moustache covered a generous mouth, hinting at his handsome appearance when a younger man. He was smartly dressed in blue-mixture woollen trousers and waistcoat, black and blue diagonal and diamond mixture sack coat, blue plaid woollen shirt and short wellington boots with calfskin feet and legs of morocco leather. With a full black satin cravat secured by a gold and agate pin, he was an imposing sight.

As they stood on deck, Thomas Miller was reminded of the smells and noises of a steam ship getting ready for her maiden voyage. There was a sulphurous tinge to the air from the smoke issuing from her two funnels. The hiss of steam escaping from the steam pipes was accompanied by a dull banging sound coming from below where the firemen were shovelling coal into her four giant boilers, and a slapping sound from the current as the tide flooding into the Mersey swept past them at anchor. There was a smell of newness: varnish, paint and polish.

They crossed the deck and went down the companion way to the cabins under the poop deck at the stern. The main cabin was very grand, with high quality fittings. Quite a crowd was there already: officers and passengers. The stewards were very attentive and the choice of food and beverage was as in a good hotel. It was a cold January morning, but with steam up, the cabin area was comfortably warm.

Conversation turned to the weather. It was not too windy but the sky was ominous. The barometer showed extremely low pressure, so there was a storm system nearby, but the storm warning signal had not been hoisted. They were waiting for the Liverpool pilot to come aboard before setting off.

Soon the pilot, William Williams, arrived and the order was given to proceed. From the cabin they could hear the shouts of the men and rattle of the chain as the anchors were raised, then the impressive noise as her two giant engines started turning. There was a slow thudding as the pistons moved up and down and lots of hissing as the valves let steam in and out of the cylinders. The paddle wheels made a thrashing noise as they swept the water astern. She was under way.

There were few onlookers on this cold winter morning; no fanfare, brass band, synchronised hooting or any such display. She slipped quietly out of the Mersey, heading for a clandestine rôle in the American Civil War.

Commander Arthur Sinclair
(courtesy of the Dickey family).

Chapter 2

Arthur Sinclair, naval officer

Arthur Sinclair was an experienced officer in the US navy. He had been promoted rapidly and was a Commander by the age of 35. When the Southern States seceded in 1861, he was in a dilemma. He and his family were from Norfolk in Virginia, which was one of the states forming the breakaway Confederacy. His colleagues in the US navy would predominantly be aligned with the Union side, representing the status quo. With the declaration of a naval blockade of the South by President Abraham Lincoln on 16 April 1861, the Union navy would be required to enforce this blockade and attack Confederate merchant shipping. If he resigned and presented himself to the Confederacy, he would have a very uncertain future.

His family had been established in the area of Norfolk, Virginia, since 1745 when his grandfather, the Shetland-born sea captain Arthur Sinclair, had settled there. The family had a tradition of giving their first-born son the name Arthur. Norfolk was, and is, an important naval base and each generation was closely involved in naval exploits, some glorious, some disastrous.

The second Arthur Sinclair, his father, had become a very distinguished US navy officer, with the rank of Commodore. Commodore Sinclair was associated with a disaster: the US navy was supporting a campaign to establish their northern border in the region of Lake Huron. In 1814 he commanded a force of USN sailing ships which landed men on Mackinac Island in an attempt to take it from the British and native American garrison, but this plan failed with considerable loss of life. They decided instead to leave two ships to lay siege to the island and they were able to capture the British schooner *Nancy* which was bringing supplies, although the crew of the *Nancy* managed to escape in their ship's boat and made their way to Mackinac island. The desperate garrison of Mackinac Island undertook an audacious plan to break the siege. They left the island in open boats at night and got alongside the anchored USS *Tigress*, climbed aboard and overpowered her crew. They then sailed the *Tigress* alongside the unsuspecting USS *Scorpion* and opened fire, capturing it too.

Arthur Sinclair was born on 29 November 1810, the first son of Commodore Arthur Sinclair. Arthur was encouraged by his father, the Commodore, to join the US navy and he enrolled as a midshipman in 1823 when he was only 13 years old. His mother, Sarah, died when he was 17. He was commissioned Lieutenant in 1835 and he married Lelia Imogen Dawley at Norfolk in that year. Their first son Arthur(jr), was born on 5 May 1837 and they went on to have 6 children over a 15 year period, of whom George Terry(jr) (their third son, known as Terry) was also to follow his elder brother, Arthur(jr), into the Navy.

Arthur Sinclair's younger brothers George Terry Sinclair and William Beverly Sinclair also served in the US navy. His sister Elizabeth married William Conway Whittle who was also prominent in the US Navy.

A notable event in Arthur's USN service was his command of the store ship *Supply* in the expedition to Japan 1852-54 under Commodore Matthew Perry. On this expedition, his son Arthur(jr) was aboard as a midshipman. The *Supply* carried gifts for the

Japanese, including products of United States invention and industry, intended to show the benefits which trade with the west could bring. Arthur managed the arrangements for the distribution of the presents. Arthur and his son were away for several years, during which time his wife Lelia was often without news for extended periods. When they did return, they brought many exotic oriental items which had been presented by the Emperor.

In 1855 Arthur Sinclair was promoted to the rank of Commander. He commanded the sloop USS *Vandalia* when it cruised the Pacific. In 1858 he rescued the mariners from the San Francisco clipper *Wild Wave* who had been shipwrecked on uninhabited Oeno Island. To seek help, a group of the castaways had sailed in their small boat to Pitcairn Island 100 miles away. When they got there, they found that the survivors of the mutiny of the *Bounty* had abandoned Pitcairn Island for Norfolk Island, leaving a note to that effect. Finding no-one on Pitcairn, they then built an open boat with tools they found abandoned on Pitcairn, and some of them sailed on towards Tahiti, where they finally found help, being picked up by the *Vandalia*. Commander Sinclair looked after them well and, on hearing their story, collected the remainder of the shipwrecked sailors who were still on Oeno and Pitcairn Islands.

With this extensive service in the US navy, it was a big decision to resign and join the rebel cause and fight against many of his colleagues. Some Southerners did not resign, but Arthur Sinclair did. Those who commanded US navy ships sailed them to a Northern port before resigning. Arthur Sinclair was assigned briefly to the Virginia State Navy, before being appointed a Commander in the Confederate States Navy on June 10, 1861. The officer ranks in the confederate navy were, in ascending order: midshipman, master, lieutenant, commander, captain and admiral. He was one of the two dozen highest ranking officers. His eldest son, Arthur Sinclair(jr), had returned to civilian life after his early experiences in the US navy and had married Drusilla Willet in 1857. He also now volunteered to serve in the Confederate Navy. One of his younger sons, George Terry(jr), also served in the Navy. Two of Arthur Sinclair's brothers, George Terry and William Beverley, who were US navy officers, also resigned to join the Confederate Navy.

Since the Union forces destroyed most of the naval yard in Norfolk before abandoning it to the Confederacy, there were few warships available to the Confederate Navy. Initially Arthur Sinclair was assigned the command of a shore position, Fort Norfolk, guarding the Elizabeth River in Virginia.

He then commanded the gunboat CSS *Winslow* (formerly the river steamer *Joseph E Coffee*) based at New Berne, North Carolina. He was ordered to defend Hatteras Inlet and, if feasible, to 'annoy and damage the commerce of the enemy'. In the Battle of Hatteras Inlet on August 28-29 1861, he helped to rescue some of the men from Fort Hatteras before it fell to Union forces. This successful Union action was an indication of their strategy in implementing the blockade: capturing forts which dominated the entrance to ports, so that the port was effectively closed.

The Confederate government was quick to appreciate the advantages of iron clad warships. They converted the abandoned wooden ship *Merrimac* at Norfolk by stripping her to deck level and building an iron shield for guns, creating the CSS *Virginia*. Her crew included Arthur Sinclair(jr) who was Captain's clerk. The *Merrimac/Virginia* left Norfolk and attacked the Union fleet in nearby Hampton Roads, sinking two Union warships, the frigate *Congress* and the sloop *Cumberland*. The rest of the Union fleet seemed vulnerable until the arrival of the newly designed *Monitor* with its revolving gun turret. In the ensuing 'first battle of the ironclads' in Hampton Roads on 9 March 1862, the *Merrimac/Virginia* and the USS *Monitor* exchanged fire without either overcoming the other. The threat of the *Merrimac/Virginia* was neutralised.

Potentially the biggest contribution by Arthur Sinclair to the confederate cause was his assignment to command a powerful iron warship, the CSS *Mississippi*, at New Orleans. This was important, since New Orleans was one of the few major ports in the Confederacy and it controlled the trade up the Mississippi River. Overall responsibility for the Confederate naval defence of New Orleans lay with Captain Whittle, brother-in-law to Arthur Sinclair. The CSS *Mississippi* was built by Nelson and Asa Tift in a new shipyard they opened in nearby Jefferson City. Construction started in October 1861 and she was still under construction in April 1862. She was strongly built with a hull two to three feet thick and with iron cladding. Because of the limited shipbuilding expertise available (the Tifts had never built a ship before), her hull shape was all straight lines and, because of her great weight, her engines, even with sixteen boilers and triple screw propulsion, were most probably inadequate, though they were never tested. According to Sinclair, she was the finest ship he had seen and she would clear not just the river Mississippi of blockading ships but would raise the blockade of all other southern ports.

When Sinclair took command on 3 April 1862, the *Mississippi* was not yet complete. She was launched on 19 April and he started to train crew to operate her, so that she could make an impact as soon as she was finished. Despite working round the clock, there were still a few more weeks of work needed. New Orleans was defended by forts and by rafts strung across the river. They hoped that these might hold up a Union attack long enough to enable them to finish the *Mississippi*, so she could play an important rôle with her intended armament of 22 guns mounted behind a strong iron shield.

The Union attack on New Orleans by Farragut on 24 April 1862 overwhelmed these defences rapidly. Arthur Sinclair obtained two steam tugs *St. Charles* and *Peytona* and he used them to try to tow the unfinished CSS *Mississippi* upriver. It was springtime and the fresh water current coming downstream was too strong. Only by creeping up close to the banks could they get back to her original mooring. Arthur Sinclair then went in the *Peytona* to New Orleans to seek additional tugs to help them, but without success since the city was being abandoned. He had left instructions with Lieutenant Waddell to set the *Mississippi* on fire should the Union forces appear, so their opponents would not be able to make use of her. When he returned, he found her on fire, as ordered. Arthur Sinclair had been very optimistic about the potential strength of the *Mississippi* but, instead of naval victories, he had to escape up river to the Confederate stronghold of Vicksburg aboard the *Peytona*. There was an inquiry into the failure to complete the CSS *Mississippi* in time to be of service, and Arthur Sinclair was among those called to give evidence. Although everyone was exonerated, he must have been frustrated and disappointed that nothing came of the efforts to build a significant warship.

One of the most successful naval exploits from the Confederate point of view, was the purchase by their European naval agent, James Bulloch, of the iron screw SS *Fingal* in Glasgow. He had her loaded with 14000 rifles, ammunition, 3000 cavalry sabres and other military stores. He made for Savannah and, after running aground while avoiding sunken ships, arrived safely in November 1861 with the very important cargo. The Union blockading force controlled the narrow shipping channel into Savannah, so that the lightly armed merchant vessel *Fingal* could not safely escape. She was commanded for several months in early 1862 by Lieutenant George Terry Sinclair, Arthur's brother, before he was posted to Glasgow to oversee construction of a new confederate warship.

When more ships were sunk to block the channel further, the decision was made to convert SS *Fingal* into an ironclad warship: the CSS *Atlanta*. The Tifts were again hired to make the transformation. She was armed with four guns and a percussion torpedo could be fitted to a projecting ram at the bow. The additional armour and guns gave her a deeper draft, 16 ft, and she was very difficult to steer. There were problems with leaks and conditions aboard were unpleasant in hot weather since she had no effective ventilation. She was commanded by Arthur Sinclair, from February to May 1863. After the failure to complete the ironclad *Mississippi*, Arthur Sinclair now had the satisfaction of commanding a formidable warship. On 3 April which was a spring tide, Arthur Sinclair took the *Atlanta* down river from Savannah, but with her deep draft, she ran aground for 12 hours at a narrow part of the channel, though she suffered little damage. Finally, on 17 June 1863, under the command of Lieutenant William Webb with a crew comprised mainly of army soldiers, she passed the obstructions and engaged the blockading forces. Because of her deep draft, she was very difficult to manoeuvre and she ran aground again. The US Monitors *Weehawken* and *Nahant* were able to fire at her at will because she could not turn to point her guns at them. *Atlanta* was forced to surrender. The Union was able to refloat the *Atlanta* and she was towed to Hampton Roads where she was used as an ironclad gunboat. Yet again the Confederate plans to combat the Union blockade had failed.

After being involved in two unsuccessful attempts to create an effective confederate iron-clad warship, Arthur Sinclair would have been very happy to hear news of a successful operation, especially as his family was closely involved. The CSS *Alabama* was ordered by Bulloch and built by Lairds at Birkenhead. She sailed, unarmed, from Liverpool under the command of Captain Mathew Butcher to a prearranged rendezvous at Terceira in the Azores. Here she picked up her armament from the barque *Agrippina* which arrived from London. She also took on board additional crew, including her commander, from the SS *Bahama* which came from Liverpool. The *Alabama* was commanded by Captain Semmes and commenced her attacks on Union shipping in August 1862. Her fourth lieutenant was Arthur Sinclair(jr) and one of her midshipmen was William Henry Sinclair, son of George T. Sinclair, Arthur's brother. One of the ships she captured, on 19 June 1863, was the barque *Conrad* which was then armed and commissioned as the CSS *Tuscaloosa*. The CSS *Tuscaloosa* under the command of John Low also captured Union shipping, her crew included William H. Sinclair now promoted to executive master. After the *Tuscaloosa* was impounded at Cape Town, William Sinclair travelled to France and attempted, along with his father George Sinclair, to join the *Alabama* as she faced a sea-battle on leaving Cherbourg. The French authorities would not allow this. So the *Alabama* left Cherbourg to confront the USS *Kearsage* with only one Sinclair aboard: Arthur(jr). In the ensuing combat off Cherbourg on 19th June 1864 *Alabama* was sunk. Many of her crew, including Arthur Sinclair(jr), were picked up by the British steam yacht *Deerhound* and taken to Southampton. During her years of commerce raiding, *Alabama* had captured or sunk over 60 Union vessels.

Lieutenant Arthur Sinclair (jr)

The next posting of Arthur Sinclair was to special service in Richmond. Richmond was the centre of government for the confederacy and was at the head of navigation of the James River. One of the priorities was to stop Union ships coming up the James River from their base in Hampton Roads. A notable naval activity at

Richmond was development by the Submarine Battery Service of inventions by Hunter Davidson and Matthew Maury of submarine mines, submarine torpedoes and other innovative naval weapons. Arthur Sinclair admired Hunter Davidson and they became close friends. The confederate navy had considerable success with mines, triggered either by contact or by electric cable. Mines were very helpful in defending the James River. Lieutenant Davidson showed great courage and initiative when on 9 April 1864, he commanded the torpedo boat *Squib* which successfully exploded a spar torpedo (an explosive charge on a long shaft at the bow of the low narrow steam boat) in contact with the steam frigate USS *Minnesota*. This exploit led to his promotion to the rank of commander and he was sent to Europe to obtain materials to build better underwater weapons.

A similar spar torpedo was used by the first submarine to sink an enemy warship. As a submarine, the CSS *Hunley* had design faults and her crews had to learn by experience. Twice she sank in harbour, killing most of her crew and her inventor, Mr. Hunley. Such was the desperate need to raise the blockade of Charleston that a third crew volunteered. Her armament was a torpedo which was mounted on a long shaft at the bow. The bigger Union warships were protected by nets from such attack. However, she did sink the wooden-hulled USS *Housatonic* with her bow-mounted torpedo off Charleston on 17 February 1864, albeit by staying partly on the surface and then subsequently sinking with the loss of all of her third crew.

After special service at Richmond, Arthur Sinclair was assigned to a blockade runner, *Mary Celestia*, carrying much needed supplies between Bermuda and Wilmington. *Mary Celestia* had been built by Messrs Miller & Sons, shipbuilders at Liverpool. She was not the first ship they had built which was to play a big rôle in the Confederate cause.

Chapter 3

The Miller family, shipbuilders

Thomas Miller had been with his father William in the office off Sefton Street of their Liverpool shipbuilding company in June 1861 when they received an attractive proposition. Their neighbours, the old established engineering company of Fawcett and Preston, had agreed to provide the engines for a new ship and offered the Millers the subcontract for the hull and fittings. This was to be the start of something quite remarkable, taking them into a world of intrigue, innovative ship design, expansion and eventually disaster.

Liverpool had a well earned reputation for innovation. The port, on the east bank of the Mersey estuary, developed from a tidal creek that offered some shelter. To overcome the limitations caused by the big tidal range (of up to 10 metres) and the vulnerability of ships anchored in the Mersey off Liverpool to a northwesterly gale, an enclosed dock accessed by a lock gate was built in 1715. This was one of the first tidal docks built anywhere and the security this gave led to a rapid growth of the port.

Liverpool recognised the importance of steam power early, the first steamship appeared in 1815 and was a Clyde-built vessel. Two years later, the first steamship was built at Liverpool, a Mersey ferry with engines from the works of Fawcett & Preston. Connection with the rest of northwest England was initially by barges (called Mersey flats) sailing to the upper Mersey. Canals were constructed inland from the tidal Mersey and, in 1830, the first important railway to be built anywhere in the world was the railway linking Liverpool and Manchester. Liverpool was well placed to utilise steam power, being close to the Lancashire coalfield.

By the 1860's the Docks were extensive and well designed, ranging from Toxteth Dock in the south to Canada Dock to the north. The centre of Liverpool was the Landing Stage, located then as now. There were no 'Three Graces' then , the area inland of the Landing Stage was mainly occupied by several small docks. The most impressive building on the waterfront would have been the Albert Dock warehouse , built in 1846. The Town Hall was much as it is now, at the end of Castle Street. St. George's Hall at that time was an impressive building in Derby Square, since demolished and replaced later by the neo-classical building near Lime Street. Another important building, also now demolished, was the Custom House in Canning Place.

The area of Liverpool around Rodney Street, Upper Parliament Street and Abercromby Square was then, as now, filled with impressive Georgian-style houses. Charles Prioleau, head of the Liverpool operations of shipping brokers Fraser Trentholm & Co., lived at 19 Abercromby Square, where the staircase still bears decoration showing a Southern US influence. William C. Miller lived at 107 Upper Parliament Street, while his son, Thomas, lived nearby at 98 Windsor Street. There were also large areas, as now, of more modest housing.

Liverpool was not just an import/export town. There were a large number of shipyards and engineering works in Liverpool. In March 1864 33 ships, totalling over 25000 tons, were under construction. As well as the Liverpool side of the Mersey, the Birkenhead side (west side) also had docks and shipyards. Because of the rapid growth of Liverpool, many of the dockers, shipyard workers and seamen came from other parts of Britain and Ireland. It was a very cosmopolitan city.

William Cowley Miller and his wife
(courtesy of Richard Harris)

William Cowley Miller was a native of Plymouth, who worked as a shipwright in the Naval Dock. He and his family, then including three children (sons William and Thomas and daughter Margaret) moved in 1836 to the booming town of Liverpool where he was employed as foreman at a shipbuilding yard. He prospered and, within a few years, he set up a business jointly with Thomas Miller Mackay. They built wooden sailing ships including, in the early 1850's, some famous trans-oceanic passenger vessels for the Black Ball line. By this time William C. Miller's family had increased with

Liverpool in 1859 from the South. The Shipyards of Jones Quiggin and of W. C. Miller & Sons are at the bottom.

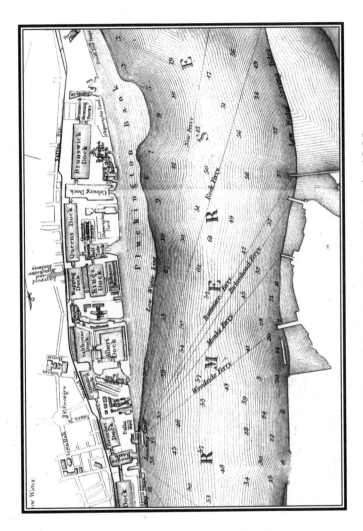

Map of Liverpool South Docks in 1864

three more children, sons Henry and Edwin and daughter Catherine. Thomas Mackay took more of an interest in shipowning and, after a few years, William C. Miller commenced business as Miller & Sons, a family shipyard. William C. Miller was highly regarded as a shipbuilder. Following his advice to the government in drawing up the bill to regulate tonnage measurements, he had been appointed to oversee the application of tonnage measurements to all ships built on the Mersey. He was elected councillor for South Toxteth in 1863. His son Thomas Lodwick, born in 1835, took a leading role in the business, and was being groomed by his father to be his successor. Thomas married Mary Keverigan, the daughter of a timber merchant, and had two sons, Thomas and Edward. Two more of William C. Miller's sons, Henry and Edwin, were active in the family business.

The shipyard of Messrs. William C. Miller and Sons had its entrance from Sefton St. near Brunswick and Toxteth docks, to the south of the centre of Liverpool, which, at that time, was at the edge of the urban area. There were slipways directly into the Mersey, graving docks (dry docks) at the end of Brunswick dock and the small Toxteth dock near Harrington town quay was used as a fitting out area. They described themselves as shipbuilders in wood and iron. Fawcett & Co. had their engineering works nearby in York Street. Their rivals, Jones Quiggin & Co., had their shipyard near to that of Millers, but further south. A sketch and an engraving show ships being launched from these slipways.

Fawcett and Preston, known on Merseyside as 'Fossets', had its origins in the Phoenix iron foundry set up in Liverpool in 1758. One of their earliest products was three-legged iron kettles and pots, many of which were exported from Liverpool. The cliché of cannibals cooking the missionary in an iron pot was most probably fiction, but Fawcett's supplied the pot! Gradually Fawcett's built up a lucrative business. An important part was supplying engines, machinery, cannon and rifles to America. When the Civil War began, the Southern states of the Confederacy had no significant heavy industry, so they looked to their traditional supplier. The Confederate naval commander James Bulloch was sent to England in 1861 to acquire naval vessels for the confederacy to counter the Union naval force blockading Southern ports and also to retaliate by acting as commerce raiders attacking Union ships worldwide. He approached Fawcett's and they agreed to act as main contractors for one vessel. The *Oreto*, as she was known at first, was to be built without any equipment of war aboard and with no obvious link to the Confederacy. In this way Bulloch kept within English law, which required England to be neutral in the Civil War, and did not allow any direct provision of war material to either side. Fawcett's offered the subcontract to Miller's to build the hull and fit out the boat, with Fawcett's providing the engines and some machinery. The guns to arm her would also be provided by Fawcett's, but in a clandestine way.

William C. Miller was the member of the Liverpool Council for South Toxteth and was a supporter of the Liberal Party. He was not sympathetic to the Confederate cause, politically, but regarded the contract to build a ship as purely a business proposition. Millers accepted the proposal from Fawcett's to build the hull of the *Oreto*.

William had experience of naval ship construction and he based the design of the *Oreto* on that of a British dispatch gunboat. By this date wooden construction was becoming obsolete, in favour of iron, in British shipyards, but, since no effective anti-fouling existed for iron hulls, they had to be cleaned in dry dock regularly. Wood, however, could be copper sheathed which gave lasting protection. The *Oreto* had a wooden hull, so she would be independent of dry docks, and was a 3-masted topsail schooner. After making some small changes to the design, James Bulloch was satisfied that she would be a very able performer in her chosen rôle. She was strongly built to carry heavy loads on deck (such as guns) and could provide berths for a large crew. Fawcett's provided horizontal direct-acting steam engines driving an iron screw which could be raised out of the water so that she would sail better without the drag of a propeller. She was completed in 1862. Union spies in Liverpool had noted what was happening and they reported that the *Oreto* was built in such a way as to be very suitable for conversion into a gun boat. Despite Union suspicions, a customs inspection showed she had no war material on board.

Bulloch had arranged that the *Oreto* was officially owned by a local agent of an Italian firm and she was registered as British with a properly certified British master and crew. The Millers knew an ideal person to act as her master for the delivery. This was Captain James Alexander Duguid, a native of Torpoint, who had moved to Liverpool, marrying William C. Miller's daughter Margaret in 1851, the year that he obtained his master's certificate. Under his command, the *Oreto* could not be legally detained. Just to make sure, the *Oreto* left Liverpool on 22 March 1862 for a trial run with ladies aboard. They were then put aboard a tender to go ashore and Bulloch's agent John Low announced that the *Oreto* was continuing to sea and that her destination was not Palermo in Italy, but Nassau in the Bahamas. Low reported very favourably on her performance at sea, in particular her solid build and her speed under sail and under steam power.

At Nassau, she was again delayed by Union claims but eventually was cleared and put to sea under the command of Capt. Duguid with Confederate officers aboard, listed as passengers. The guns, equipment and stores constructed by Fawcett's and needed for her conversion to a gunboat had been brought separately from Liverpool by the steamer *Bahama*. The *Oreto* could not be armed in a neutral port, so these items were then put aboard the schooner *Prince Albert* which sailed out to sea to meet up with the *Oreto*. The transfer took place at sea near a remote island, Green Cay, and was very hard work for the crew under the hot sun. But finally, in early August 1862, the CSS *Florida* (as she was now called) was commissioned under the command of Lieutenant John Maffitt. The seamen on *Florida* were offered the chance to remain on board, sharing the risks and the prize money, or to return to Nassau aboard the *Prince Albert*. Most accepted the challenge. One of her junior officers was midshipman George Terry Sinclair(jr), third son of Arthur Sinclair.

Her career started badly. The crew was struck down with yellow fever with both John Maffitt and Terry Sinclair among those affected. The equipment taken on board lacked important items, so that her guns could not be operated effectively. She called at Cuba briefly to pick up supplies and some more crew. With few healthy crew aboard, Maffitt decided to run the blockade into Mobile. He, himself, was ill and could hardly stand. To be sure of finding the channel, he approached in daylight, flying the British ensign. The USS *Oneida* and *Winona* were blockading and ordered the approaching ship to stop. Maffitt then hoisted the Confederate flag and ran between the blockading ships. The crew of *Florida* were too weak from yellow fever to deploy their own guns and they had to suffer heavy gunfire for 20 minutes until they got under the covering fire of Fort Morgan. The ship was riddled with shells and shrapnel but only one man was killed.

It took several months to repair the damage and her commander then waited until there was an offshore gale to give them the best chance to escape. On the night of 15 January 1863, *Florida* set out. There were now eleven blockading ships and, by star light, she managed to steam quietly past several until her smoke was blown across the deck of a blockader which flashed a bright light to alert the others. Aboard *Florida*, men were aloft ready to deploy sails and the order was given to set all sail. With full sail set rapidly and her engines at full power, she had a good start on the blockaders. The only USN vessel fast enough to keep up with her was the gunboat USS *R.R. Cuyler*. *Florida* was able to achieve a speed of 13.6 knots with the strong following wind. After a day-long chase, she was able to outrun the *R.R. Cuyler*. This performance was a testimony to her design by Millers.

The intention was not to take on the US Navy (which hugely outnumbered the Confederate Navy) but to prey upon Union merchant vessels. Having escaped from Mobile, CSS *Florida* roamed the Atlantic capturing Union ships. She sailed under a British flag, until close to her target when she raised the Confederate flag. Since the Confederate ports were blockaded, any Union ships she captured could not be sent there and so were burned or bonded (forced to pay a fine, but allowed to proceed). The clipper *Jacob Bell* with a cargo valued at $1.5 million was the most valuable capture. The crew benefited from a share of any prize money. One constraint was that she was only allowed to take on board limited supplies in neutral ports, and she did not visit any home ports, although she was able to obtain some provisions and coal from ships she captured. On one occasion a Union gunboat came close to her but, by lowering her funnels, she was able to modify her appearance and escape a confrontation. After an enforced period in port at Brest in France to refit the ship, the *Florida* returned to the offensive and

CSS Florida runs the blockade into Mobile in 1862

captured in total 38 Union ships. On 10 July 1864, she captured the *Electric Spark* off Delaware. While transferring the money safe in a small boat at night from the *Electric Spark*, the boat was swamped and sank. Midshipman William B. Sinclair(jr), who was in charge of the boat, grabbed an oar, but when a sailor shouted that he could not swim, he unselfishly gave him the oar. Though William could swim he did not survive. He had joined the *Florida* in early 1864 while still in his teens and was the son of Arthur Sinclair's brother, William Beverley Sinclair, who held the rank of surgeon in the CS Navy.

One of the most exciting episodes occurred when Lieutenant Charles Read suggested in mid 1863 that he be allowed to take command of the brig *Clarence* which had just been captured by the *Florida* and operate her as an additional armed cruiser. His plan was to enter the Union base at Chesapeake Bay using her genuine papers and registry and then cause mayhem. He fitted her with wooden dummy guns and added gun ports, even though they only had one 6 pounder aboard. He captured several valuable Union merchantmen and, on board one, he learnt that only ships with cargoes for the Federal Government were allowed to proceed to the base in Hampton Roads. It was time to change plan. Read, ever adventurous, sought a faster ship than the sluggish *Clarence*. He sighted the *Tacony* and was only able to get close to her by the deception of flying a distress signal. He now moved his operations and gun to the *Tacony*. He then burned the *Clarence* which created a most impressive aroma - she had a cargo of coffee beans. His predation continued. By now a Union fleet of warships were searching for the non-existent *Clarence*, and Read on the *Tacony* was even stopped once or twice by Union warships and asked if he had seen the *Clarence*. To keep up the deception, he then moved his operation to a small schooner, the *Archer*. Since he was out of ammunition, he took her into harbour at Portland, Maine, where, at night, he captured the USN cutter *Caleb Cushing* as her crew were asleep and sailed out in her. Before he could capture another ship and cover his tracks, a hastily assembled flotilla of Union armed ships approached. His luck now evaporated and he was out-gunned and forced to set her on fire and surrender. He had captured 22 vessels by his initiative using only a small band of men and one large gun. He had tied up a huge fleet of Union warships - looking for a ship that no longer existed. He was later exchanged with Union prisoners of war and promoted to the rank of Commander.

The *Florida* and the armed raiders she created (such as the *Clarence/Tacony*) captured over 60 Union merchant ships between them. The *Florida* is less well known than another Mersey-built commerce raider, the *Alabama* (then known as *Enrica*), built by Lairds. She had been ordered by Bulloch a few weeks after the *Oreto/Florida* but commenced her attacks on Union shipping in August 1862, so she started operations before the *Florida*. She also captured over 60 Union merchant ships. Although it was a great satisfaction to the Confederate navy that they were compensating for the Union navy attacks on unarmed blockade runners, the main financial impact of the Confederate armed cruisers was to increase the insurance rates for US merchant vessels, so benefiting Britain since British vessels were not attacked.

The publicity surrounding these two Confederate Navy vessels, *Florida* and *Alabama*, built on Merseyside, meant it was going to be difficult for the Miller shipyard to build warships for eventual use by the Confederacy. As well as building ships for the domestic trade (for example the steam tug *Emperor*), Millers were again asked to build a ship as a subcontract from Fawcett's. She was intended to be a gift to the Confederate government from Fraser, Trentholm & Company, cotton brokers and ship-owners whose Liverpool agent was Charles Prioleau. The small wooden vessel *Alexandra* was very strongly built with a steam engine to power her propeller and a three-masted barquentine rig. At 145 feet long, she was smaller than the *Florida* which was 191 feet long. She was described by Millers as suitable for use as a yacht or mailboat, though she was very suitable for conversion into a gunboat. She was launched on 7

Alexandra

March 1863 by Mrs William Miller, named *Alexandra* after the Princess who married the Prince of Wales on 10 March, and was then fitted out in Toxteth Dock.

Although Miller's shipyard was surrounded by a high wall and entry was controlled, it was common knowledge that the *Alexandra* had links to the Confederacy, since a report in the newspapers on 16 March stated 'a gunboat built by Messrs W C Miller & Sons at Liverpool for the Confederates was launched last week'. Before she could sail, the Union consul, Thomas Dudley, in Liverpool used Union agents to support this allegation and he placed their evidence before the British government. The *Alexandra* was arrested on 5 April 1863. The Union spies were motivated by payment and were a rather disreputable bunch of men. Much of their evidence was hearsay and not legally significant. Sometimes they were just plain wrong. One of the spies was John Da Costa who described himself as a shipowner and shipping agent, although he was actually a partner in a tug, the SS *Emperor* being built by Millers alongside the *Alexandra*. His evidence was that he had heard Thomas Miller state that *Alexandra* was intended as a Confederate gunboat and that he had seen Captain Tessier, who had worked for Fraser Trentholm for many years, discussing the construction of her. Another man gave evidence that several people present at her launch, Charles Prioleau, Captain Tessier and some clerks, all had close links with Fraser Trenholm. Another spy, George Temple Chapman, had presented himself at Fraser Trentholm's Liverpool office and had volunteered to aid the Confederate cause. He had a conversation with Charles Prioleau, and a brief meeting with James Bulloch, but he was unable to trap them into any rash disclosure. The third main source of evidence came from Clarence Randolf Yonge who had been a trusted Confederate naval officer: the paymaster on the *Alabama*. His reliability as a witness was questioned, since he had deserted and entrapped a widow for her money, subsequently abandoning her and her children. He gave evidence about the funding of the *Alabama*.

The evidence presented was that *Alexandra* was very suitable for conversion to a warship (which was true) and that she would be converted into a Confederate warship (which was not proven). After a year-long series of court proceedings, in May 1864 she was eventually cleared on condition that she was clearly fitted out as a merchant vessel. Named *Mary*, Captain Edward Montgomery Collier took her from Liverpool on 17 July and arrived off St. George's Harbour in Bermuda on 30 August. Yellow fever was rife there at that time, so he returned to Halifax. She returned to Bermuda on 14 November 1864 and then left for Nassau, arriving on 29 November. Here she took on coal. Union spies reported seeing guns on board, so she was again the subject of court proceedings. One gun (built by Fawcett & Preston) was found among the goods stowed aboard, but she was released on 30 May 1865, too late for her to play any rôle in the Civil War. The Union diplomatic service had lost the court cases but they had scored a victory: they had eliminated the contribution of the *Alexandra*.

The legal proceedings over the *Alexandra* clarified the possibilities for Confederate agents to acquire vessels suitable for conversion to warships. Bulloch had contracted with Lairds in Birkenhead for two ironclads (known as the Laird rams) and George Sinclair (Arthur Sinclair's brother) had arranged for an ironclad, the *Pampero (Texas)*, to be built at Glasgow. As these plans came to light, the vessels were detained on British Government instructions and played no rôle in the Civil War.

Since the Miller family shipyard had built two ships which were intended as Confederate warships, the Union spies kept a very close watch over them. There was another type of ship much in demand - the blockade runner - and that was to be their next involvement with the American Civil war.

Chapter 4

Liverpool builds blockade runners

In the early years of the Civil War, the Union blockade was quite ineffective and most trading vessels were able to get through unharmed. As the Union built up its naval forces and as more Confederate ports were lost, the blockade became more effective. Special ships, known as blockade runners, transferred goods between Southern ports and neutral ports: mainly Nassau in the Bahamas or Bermuda, which were about 600 miles distant. These goods (mainly cotton and tobacco as exports and military supplies, clothing and meat as imports) were carried across the Atlantic, mainly from Liverpool, in slower and more cost-effective vessels, either deep-draft iron steamships or sailing ships.

Liverpool was a natural base for Confederate operations in Europe, since most of the valuable cotton was landed there. Trading firms such as Fraser Trentholm were able to provide cash and indeed effectively operated as bankers to the Confederacy. Their Liverpool manager, Charles Prioleau, was responsible for ordering suitable shipping, for arranging cargoes and for buying and selling the merchandise carried.

The most successful blockade runners were found to be those built as Clyde river steamers. These were fast iron paddle steamers with a relatively shallow draft so that they could get into the shallows away from the deeper draft blockading USN ships. They had a low profile, so that they could not be seen from far away. To aid their chances of avoiding detection, they burnt specially chosen coal (Welsh anthracite) which gave out as little smoke as possible. They sometimes had funnels that could be reduced in height by tilting or telescoping, and their upper masts could be removed. They needed to carry enough coal in their bunkers for at least a three day run at high speed.

To maintain neutrality and the protection of the British flag, blockade runners being delivered from Britain were registered as British with a properly certified master and crew. Thomas Miller's brother-in-law, Captain James Duguid, who had delivered the *Oreto/Florida* to Nassau was one of those who provided this delivery service. He delivered the Clyde-built paddle steamers *Giraffe* (later renamed *Robert E Lee*) to Charleston in late December 1862 and the *Juno(I)* (later renamed *Helen*) to Nassau in July 1863.

As the supply of second-hand Clyde paddle steamers became exhausted, shipyards on the Mersey began to design ships specially suited for blockade running. One innovation that attracted them was the use of steel rather than iron. This would allow a much lighter vessel for the same overall size: giving more cargo space and greater speed. At that time, steel was expensive and it was difficult to obtain large amounts of good quality. One of the first steel steamships had been the small riverboat *Ma Robert* built by Lairds on the Mersey in 1858 to be exported to Africa for Dr. Livingstone's expedition. In 1863 the Mersey shipyards produced the first ocean-going steel ships. The honour of being the first steel ship to cross the Atlantic goes to the *Banshee(I)*, a paddle steamer built by Jones, Quiggin & Co., whose yard was close to that of Millers. At the same time Millers built the *Phantom*, a steel screw steamship of length 193 feet with engines by Fawcett Preston. She was the second steel ship to cross the Atlantic. Millers pioneered what was to become the basic ship design until the present day: steel hull with screw propulsion.

With all the unfavourable attention to their yard because of the *Florida* and *Alexandra*, Millers had decided to build merchant vessels suited for use as blockade runners, for which there was now a strong demand. They may have expected to avoid the attention of Union spies, but they were wrong. The *Phantom* was launched around 15 March 1863, shortly after the launch of the *Alexandra*. This coincidence, togther with Millers' previous association with Confederate naval ships, encouraged Union spies to target both vessels. Union spies reported that they had seen Bulloch, the Confederate naval agent based in Liverpool, directing the building of the *Phantom* and another spy reported that a Confederate Navy officer, Captain Davidson, had arrived in Liverpool, staying in the George Hotel, and was to take charge of the *Phantom*. After launching, the *Phantom* was transferred to Clarence Graving Dock. By 6 April she was in Clarence Dock, receiving her engines and machinery with the aid of a large crane. After delays in investigating the evidence, the *Phantom* was cleared of any violation of neutrality and was registed at Liverpool on 21 May 1863, so she was only held up by a few weeks.

Phantom was delivered from Liverpool by Capt. Tessier and, on arrival in Wilmington on 15 July 1863, was bought by the Confederate Ordnance Bureau and continued blockade running under the command of Capt. Porter. He made another three runs through the blockade between Bermuda and Wilmington before being detected at daybreak on 23 September 1863, while still 50 miles off his destination of Wilmington, by the USS *Connecticut*. The USN ship chased the *Phantom* for about four hours, getting within a mile of her. The *Phantom* was running as close inshore as possible to avoid capture, but after several shots were fired, she turned sharply and ran ashore on the beach, near Rich Inlet. Her crew set her on fire, so that she could not be taken over by the Union side, and fled ashore. The USS *Connecticut* sent boats alongside but could not put the fire out. The *Connecticut* fired several shots at her to damage her further. Some salvage must have been achieved from the shore, however, since the engines and some of the cargo (arms and medicines) from the *Phantom* were recovered.

Just as the crew aboard a successful blockade runner were rewarded very well financially, so the blockading Union ships offered a substantial fraction of the prize money to their crews should they capture any Confederate runner. So patriotism was enhanced by a strong profit motive for the crews on each side. Many of the crew of blockade runners were from European ports such as Liverpool. This was even an advantage, since, if captured, they were released quickly, unlike American citizens.

A blockade runner at speed

Unlike *Phantom*, however, *Banshee(I)* was phenomenally successful, running the blockade fourteen times before capture. She was owned by a Liverpool-based company, the Anglo-Confederate

Trading Company in which the Mayor, Edward Lawrence, had a leading position, and she made them a lot of money: the investors recouped seven times their outlay. Her shipping agent, Thomas Taylor, who sailed aboard her, wrote a book describing the details of blockade running. One particularly dramatic passage was when, returning to Nassau from Wilmington on 22 September 1863, they discovered that they were being pursued by the USS *James Adger*. With a following wind the *James Adger* was gaining on them and they could clearly see the officers on her bridge. Captain Steele ordered the *Banshee(I)* upwind, even though this was taking them away from their destination. It was satisfying to see the big USN ship taking in sail. To lighten the *Banshee(I)*, they threw her valuable deck cargo of cotton bales overboard. Crashing into the waves, they now began to gain on their pursuer. The engineer Erskine reported that the bearings were becoming overheated and that they must stop the engines. This would have been surrender, so they loosened the bearings and lubricated them with what they had on board which was salad oil mixed with gunpowder. The chase lasted 15 hours until they saw the *James Adger* give up, though only five miles astern. Apparently her coal supply was low and her stokers were exhausted. She had not fired at the *Banshee(I)* because she only had broadside guns and it was too rough to move one on deck to fire forward. The *Banshee* was now off course and her coal supply was low. They had to burn the wood from the bulkheads and masts with cotton and turpentine as additional fuel, just making the safety of an isolated island of the Bahamas. Here they persuaded a schooner to go to Nassau to bring them coal, though extremely strong winds made this a challenge. The USN was eventually to prevail, however, the USS *Fulton* captured the *Banshee* on 21 November 1863 while she was trying to enter Wilmington. *Banshee* was armed and taken into the US Navy.

Both the *Banshee(I)* and *Phantom*, though pioneers of steel shipbuilding, were not quite as big an improvement as had been hoped. For various reasons they both achieved less than their design speed of 16 knots. The *Banshee(I)* was also reported as having considerable problems with leaks around her steel plates. These first steel vessels, however, were prototypes that established the principles needed to design such vessels.

Two more blockade runners were completed in Liverpool in 1863, the *Lucy* and *Wild Dayrell*, both built by Jones Quiggin. *Lucy* was a 215 feet long steel paddle steamer owned by Fraser Trentholm. She was delivered by Captain James Duguid, brother-in-law to Thomas Miller, and he remained in charge to run the blockade into Wilmington for several months from 21 November 1863 until passing control to Captain Beaton on 26 June 1864. One exciting incident was on 14 March 1864 when *Lucy* ran aground approaching Wilmington. Captain Duguid sent men ashore with important government mail. A blockader approached and fired at her, without hitting her. Colonel Jones of the shore battery at Fort Caswell realised what was needed and put two guns in place on the shore near the stranded *Lucy* to drive off the blockader, hitting her bow. Although seven blockading vessels arrived and fired at *Lucy*, the shore guns kept them away, so the *Lucy* could be refloated and escape undamaged. Another narrow escape occurred on the night of 27 May 1863, when off Wilmington, the USS *Kansas* chased the *Lucy* for four hours, gaining steadily until *Kansas* ran out of good coal and started to fall back, despite the expedient of feeding barrels of pork into her boilers to supplement the remaining poor quality coal. The *Lucy* was supposed to be carrying a large amount of gold bullion to Europe. After 21 successful runs through the blockade, *Lucy's* luck ran out on 2 November 1864 when USS *Santiago de Cuba* sighted her by moonlight leaving Wilmington in stormy weather and captured her. All the crew aboard *Lucy* were taken prisoner, including her signal officer, Sidney Lanier, later well known as a writer, musician and poet.

By contrast the *Wild Dayrell*, built by Jones Quiggin for the Liverpool-funded Anglo-Confederate Trading company had a short career, running the blockade 4 times before being deliberately run aground and destroyed north of Wilmington on 1 February 1864 when chased by the USS *Sassacus*.

The standard pattern for a blockade runner was now established: basically similar to, or larger than, the *Banshee(I)* with paddle wheels as the preferred propulsion. By 1864, the confederate government was very concerned about the reduction in vital imports because of the strengthening blockade. They realised that it was not sufficient to leave blockade running to private initiatives. Swelling the numbers of new blockade runners being built by merchants, the confederate agent in Liverpool, James Bulloch, ordered a large number of suitable ships to be built, using trading companies as a front to cover the source of the funding. Many of these were ordered from Merseyside shipyards, since the valuable exports of cotton and tobacco were mainly brought to Liverpool and provided a source of funds. Shipyards on both banks of the Mersey were busy building blockade runners. Compared to 1863 when only four Liverpool-built blockade runners were active, during 1864 at least ten new Mersey-built vessels had started to run the blockade and by the end of that year twenty more were being delivered or under construction.

Among the vessels completed in 1864, two stood out as specially impressive, the *Hope* and the *Colonel Lamb*, both ordered by Charles Prioleau of Fraser Trentholm and built of steel by Jones, Quiggin & Co. Their large size (nearer 280 ft long rather than 220 ft) meant that they could carry more bales of cotton, but more importantly, they were capable of great speed: above 15 knots which was very fast for that date. The *Hope* was launched on 25 November 1863 by Mrs Josiah Jones(jr), wife of one of the owners of the Jones Quiggin's shipyard. Ten minutes earlier, from the next slipway, a steel sailing ship *Formby*, had been launched by a Miss Mills, relative of one of her owners. Unusually the *Formby* was launched with her engine already aboard and even with steam up, so she could proceed under her own power to dock. A contemporary sketch by

Lelia

A sketch of the launch on 25th November 1863 from Jones Quiggins yard of the steel ships, Formby on the right and Hope, the paddle steamer, on the left.

-38-

William Woods shows the crowds enjoying the spectacle. The celebrations of a launch day would have been in striking contrast to the usual situation in the shipyard, with a huge din coming from the

The blockade runner Colonel Lamb

hammering of the rivetting teams, and from metal cutting, bending and drilling. As an illustration of the advantage of steel, Mr. Jones quoted at the banquet after the launch, that the *Formby* would have needed 800 tons of iron but only 500 tons of steel were used in her construction.

The *Hope* was to be fitted with engines from the Victoria Iron Works and was completed and ready to run the blockade in July 1864, under the command of Captain Hammer who had previous experience running the blockade aboard *Annie Childs*. Despite the great potential of the *Hope*, she had a poor record as a blockade runner. On her second approach to Wilmington on 22 October 1864, she was sighted and chased by the USS *Eolus*. *Hope* should have outrun this armed tug easily, but a steam pipe fractured and she was captured. The crew of the *Eolus* were well rewarded, seamen receiving a thousand dollars apiece, when their daily wage would have been about a dollar. Seamen on a blockade runner were paid around 250 dollars a trip.

The other super-runner, the *Colonel Lamb*, was launched on 26 May 1864 from Jones Quiggin's yard. Unconventionally, the wife of her intended captain performed the ceremony by being aboard as she was launched. Mrs Lockwood said that she was acting as godmother to the ship as it made its way into its native element. At the time of its trial run in October 1864, the *Colonel Lamb* raced the Irish Sea passenger SS *Douglas*, one of the fastest boats then built, achieving over 17 knots and winning convincingly. The *Colonel Lamb* was the largest steel vessel built at the time of her launch. She was designed with special features requested by her captain, Thomas Lockwood, who had extensive experience of running the blockade.

The main producer of blockade runners was the yard of Jones, Quiggin & Co., while the Miller yard built two paddle wheel blockade runners in 1864, each about 220 ft long. Perhaps because of previous experience with Union spies, the launch of these ships from Millers was not widely publicised. In contrast, other ships launched by Millers that year (a 160 ft long steamer *Gurupy* on 23 April; two 127 ft long ferry paddle boats for use on the Mersey, *Sprite* and *Sylph*, on 24 May; two 120 ft long Indian river steamers on 23 June; the 129 ft long paddle tug *Knight Templar* on 21 July) were well publicised.

One of the Miller built blockade runners, *Let her B*, which became *Chicora* as a runner, was subcontracted to Millers by Jones, Quiggin and again had engines by Fawcett Preston. She was completed at the same time as *Badger*, built by Jones Quiggin and the two ships competed against one another on their trials on 23 March 1864, each winning one leg. *Let her B* was owned by the Chicora Importing and

Exporting Company, based in Charleston. Under Capt. Holgate, she ran between Bermuda and Wilmington several times in mid 1864 and then she transferred to the Nassau to Charleston route. She ran through the blockade fourteen times and she was the last blockade runner to get into Charleston in February 1865. One interesting interlude occurred in July 1864 when she and *Florie* were chosen for their speed and good performance to be impressed into the Confederate Navy and each armed with two guns. The plan was to launch a surprise attack on the Union prison in Maryland which held Confederate prisoners. When word came that the plan was known to the Union side, it was dropped and the ships were returned to blockade running.

The other Miller built blockade runner was known as *Bijou* while being built, but registered as *Mary Celestia*. She was built for William Crenshaw & Co. William G. Crenshaw, an artillery officer and Richmond businessman, had been sent in early 1863 to Britain to arrange, in partnership with a British shipping agent, to acquire goods for the use of the Confederate Navy and War Departments. Crenshaw entered into a partnership with Alexander Collie in London. The arrangement was that the Confederacy would pay 75% and Collie and Crenshaw 12.5% each, of the cost of the ships to be built, then 50% of the cargo space would be allocated to the War Dept, 25% to the Navy Dept and the remainder to Collie & Crenshaw. Since some departments, such as Ordnance, had already made their own arrangements to import supplies, this contract caused some friction. The resolution was that Collie & Crenshaw would import quartermaster and commissionary goods such as food, clothing, shoes and tents. Crenshaw requested that the Navy Department provide commanders for these boats, but they refused to release active officers. Crenshaw employed his brother James as agent in Wilmington, but this was not well received by Collie. By early 1864, the last of the Collie & Crenshaw blockade runners had been lost and the partnership was dissolved, with each subsequently trading separately.

In November 1863, Crenshaw accepted a contract to deliver 3 million pounds of bacon. In mid 1864, Crenshaw had three blockade runners in operation: *Mary Celestia, Agnes E. Fry* and *Armstrong*. Crenshaw had been advanced £140,000 by General McRae to keep this operation afloat and he had two ships under construction: the *City of Richmond* being built in London and one under construction by Millers in Liverpool.

By 1864 the blockading Union navy was so strong that the Confederate Navy realised that it was not possible to achieve significant impact by attacking them directly. The Confederate Navy was, instead, concentrating its efforts on commerce raiders, which attacked Union merchant shipping worldwide, and on improving the success rate of vessels running the blockade. Those blockade runners which imported goods for the confederate War and Navy departments were assigned CSN officers to command them. This involved some deception: when in a neutral port the ship had to appear to be a regular British-flagged vessel, while if captured running the blockade, the CS Navy crew would only be treated as prisoners of war (rather than pirates) if the vessel showed Confederate colours.

After his posting to Richmond, Arthur Sinclair was sent to command the Liverpool-built blockade runner *Mary Celestia* which ran the blockade between Bermuda and Wilmington, North Carolina, carrying supplies for the War and Navy Departments, as agreed with Crenshaw's. Another of Crenshaw's runners, the *Agnes E Fry* was named after the wife of her captain Lieutenant Joseph Fry.

The blockade runners used the harbour at St. George at the north east end of Bermuda for transferring cargoes between the blockade runners and the ships that crossed the Atlantic, mainly from Liverpool. St.George in Bermuda was a neutral port, since it was a British colony. It had a reputation as a wild place - those who ran the blockade successfully were very well rewarded and the crews had more spending money than they had ever had before. Heavy drinking and extravagant behaviour were common, it was said that men threw money from the windows of the drinking dens to see the locals scramble for it. The atmosphere was said to be similar to the days when pirates roamed the Carribean.

At that time Wilmington, the deep water port closest to the military action, was blockaded by a substantial Union force. The reason that access was still possible was Fort Fisher. Located near the mouth of the Cape Fear river, its garrison under Colonel Lamb controlled the channel into Wilmington preventing Union ships from coming too close. The blockade runners chose a moonless night to avoid detection and often made use of their shallow draft by running close inshore at high speed. Even so, they usually received a few shots from the blockaders before they came within the covering range of Fort Fisher's guns. They were not safe on the passage between St. George's Harbour in Bermuda and Wilmington either, a good lookout was needed to enable them to keep out of sight of other ships and their low profile with dull paintwork helped. When spotted, speed was their only saviour, but by this date some of the Union vessels were equally fast.

The *Mary Celestia* successfully ran the blockade 4 times in each direction between 27 May and 24 August 1864, listed under a variety of names: *Mary Celeste, Marie Celesta,* etc. Running the blockade in and out of Wilmington, the most important man aboard was the Wilmington pilot. Captain Mike Usina had the services of a young pilot, John Anderson, who guided them safely out of Wilmington to St. Georges in Bermuda. Here they loaded up with clothing, blankets, hams and pork. Unfortunately they also took aboard something less healthy - yellow fever which was then rife in Bermuda. John Anderson was infected but, though seriously ill, he was carried on deck as they ran into Wilmington, giving the appropriate commands to get safely through the shoals as they were pursued by a blockading warship. As they anchored in the river, he died. After a period of quarantine, *Mary Celestia* took on board cotton, a new captain: Commander Arthur Sinclair CSN and a new and very experienced pilot, John Galloway. Arthur Sinclair would have been very aware of the dangers of yellow fever. His sister and her eldest son, Arthur Sinclair Whittle, had both died in the 1855 epidemic which affected Norfolk, Virginia, while his own son, George Terry, had come close to dying when infected in Bermuda aboard the CSS *Florida*. The last run through the blockade made by *Mary Celestia* was out of Wilmington on 24 August, reaching St. Georges a few days later. Yellow fever was still rampant there and John Galloway became ill and died in Bermuda on 27 September, the second Wilmington pilot of *Mary Celestia* to be lost to yellow fever.

On 26 September, *Mary Celestia* had a Bermudan pilot, John Virgin, aboard while navigating the inshore reefs near Christian Bay on the South Shore of Bermuda. It was reported that the crew under Commander Sinclair were attempting to put the pilot and the owner, Colonel Crenshaw, ashore before proceeding to Nassau with a cargo including canned meat. The first officer reported breakers ahead, but the pilot assured Captain Sinclair that he knew the coast like his own house. Well, as the Bermudan newspapers reported, perhaps he hadn't been home for a while, because she hit the Blind Breakers reef when steaming at 13 knots and soon sank. The only loss of life was the ship's cook who returned to salvage some items as she sank. The rest of the crew reached shore safely, although with yellow fever then raging in Bermuda, many did not survive. The yellow fever epidemics in Bermuda and the Bahamas each summer were a big factor in limiting the success of the blockade runners. To avoid an outbreak as happened in 1862, they were quarantined at Wilmington for up to 30 days before being allowed to unload, so could make fewer trips.

There were several suggestions circulating as to why she had hit a reef and sunk; either because of a deliberate act by the pilot who had been bribed by Union agents, or in an alcohol-fuelled accident. A song composed at the time suggests strongly the second option with its refrain

'So Johnny fill up the glass

And we'll all drink stone blind'.

The wreck of the *Mary Celestia* now lies to the southwest of Bermuda on a sandy bottom in 16 metres with her starboard paddle wheel standing prominently from the seabed, a situation that we shall meet again.

Since their blockade runner was lost and yellow fever was a serious risk at Bermuda, Arthur Sinclair and his engineer Charles Francis Middleton were directed to Liverpool to take charge of one of the new blockade runners being built there for Crenshaws, arriving from Bermuda in the autumn of 1864. Although St. George in Bermuda had grown from a sleepy village into a thriving port, the contrast with Liverpool would have been dramatic. Liverpool was a world leading port at that time.

Chapter 5

Wreck and rescue at Liverpool

Liverpool was the premier port of Britain for long distance shipping. During one day as many as 78 ships from foreign ports could arrive in the Mersey, as well as numerous coasting vessels and ferries from Ireland and the Isle of Man. Combined with the fleet of Mersey ferries, Mersey flats, tugs and boatmen taking people to and from anchored vessels, the Mersey was a very busy waterway. During the month of July 1864 alone, over 8000 passengers emigrated to North America on ships bound from Liverpool, many of them having come from the continent of Europe by train and ferry. As well as these passengers, Liverpool was full of seamen - over 70,000 registered seamen embarked on ships each year.

The port of Liverpool was run by the Mersey Docks and Harbour Board. They were very concerned with safety and the channel into Liverpool was marked by lightships, buoys and lighthouses which they maintained. They also surveyed and dredged the shipping channel. There were many pilots to guide the large number of vessels in and out. They transferred to incoming vessels from (and from outgoing vessels to) pilot boats that cruised offshore for extended periods. The MDHB employed crews for lifeboats stationed around the area. Liverpool had been a pioneer of lifeboat services, arranged to suit the local conditions.

***Ships leaving the Mersey in March 1861,
after several days of adverse winds***

The approaches to the Mersey are strewn with sandbanks and in onshore winds there are breaking waves along the edges of the banks. Ships that were driven onto the banks were at the mercy of the waves and many lives were lost. The strong currents running between the sandbanks caused problems for sailing ships and when wind and tide were in different directions, steep waves built up in the channel. The approaches to the Mersey are especially dangerous in Northwesterly gales. The best way to rescue shipwrecked sailors was recognised to be by using small boats that could venture into the shallow waters around a stranded vessel. If such a boat could get upwind of the wreck and then anchor, by veering out line it would be possible to come to her assistance in a controlled way. The small boats used were of the type used as local fishing boats and gigs. They had sails that could be set when conditions allowed but they relied on a number of men aboard with oars. The men were usually local fishermen with experience of such boats and of the local conditions. To be out in storm conditions in these small open boats must have been terrifying but men to crew them were readily found.

The boats were based at places where a boat could be launched from the shore in strong winds. In the Liverpool Bay area, this implied from within the more sheltered waters of the Mersey itself or from Hoylake or Formby which both had an inshore channel protected by an offshore sandbank except at the top of the tide. Such rescue attempts were not conducted by dedicated lifeboats until experience showed that this was the best and safest way.

Liverpool was the site of the first dedicated lifeboat station to be established anywhere in the world. This was at Formby in 1776 and was funded by the Dock Trustees. Subsequently a lifeboat station was established at Hoylake around 1803 and a lifeboat was kept at the mouth of the Mersey itself. The Dock Trustees were charged with responsibility for safety in the approaches to the Port of Liverpool. As a result of a formal inquiry into the state of lifeboats in 1823, it was recommended that four boats be provided: at Formby, Hoylake, Point of Ayr and the Magazines (near New Brighton). The lifeboat at the Magazines was established around 1827. After the poor showing of the lifeboat service during the hurricane of 1839, the arrangements were changed and a later report in 1843 gave the situation as 9 lifeboats: namely 2 at Liverpool, 2 at the Magazines, 2 at Hoylake, 2 at Point of Ayr and 1 at Formby.

In 1858 the Mersey Docks and Habour Board took over from the Dock Trustees the provision of 8 lifeboats at Liverpool, New Brighton, Hoylake, Formby, Southport and Point of Ayr. From 1848 one of the Hoylake lifeboats had been stationed at Hilbre Island. As well as the MDHB lifeboats, a RNLI lifeboat station was established at New Brighton in 1863 - this usually had two lifeboats which lay afloat and were reached by a boarding punt from the New Brighton landing stage. The same arrangement was used for the Liverpool lifeboats of the MDHB based near the Liverpool landing stage.

This lifeboat service was very efficient and saved very many lives as had been recognised in 1851 when the RNLI (named National Institute for Preservation of Life from Shipwreck, at that time) awarded silver medals for outstanding bravery to the coxswains of all of these lifeboats. Each station had a permanent crew of about 10 men and shore-based boats were launched by carriage pulled by horses kept nearby. The crew was summoned by gun and it was claimed that the lifeboat could be under way in 17 or 18 minutes from receiving the signal of distress. The location of the distress was given by code flags which identified the area since Liverpool Bay was divided into small square areas with numbers assigned to each. The lifeboats had oars and could be sailed, but, to speed up rescue by the lifeboats kept afloat, an arrangement existed with the tug companies to tow the first available lifeboat to the ship in distress.

Despite every precaution, there had been several serious accidents involving loss of lifeboat crew in the years leading up to 1865.

Point of Ayr, at the mouth of the Dee estuary was the site of a lifeboat station maintained by the Dock Board. A disaster in 1857 highlighted the problem of communication. Two lifeboats independently went to the rescue of the same vessel so that the loss of one lifeboat was futile. On 4 January 1857 the schooner *Temperance* was driven ashore near Abergele. Her distress signals were seen by the Rhyl and Point of Ayr lifeboat stations early in the morning. The Point of Ayr lifeboat proceeded under sail to the west in squally weather. As she passed Rhyl, an unusually heavy sea struck her, she capsized and did not right herself. The men who had launched the Rhyl lifeboat saw the Point of Ayr lifeboat capsize not far offshore and, unable to help, they saw the crew, one by one, swept off the upturned boat in the bitterly cold conditions until eventually all 13 were lost. The men were not wearing their cork lifejackets. The Rhyl lifeboat, which was stationed nearer to the wreck site, had already been launched so the tragic rescue mission by the Point of Ayr lifeboat was not even necessary. This remains the most serious lifeboat disaster to have occurred in North Wales.

As well as the lifeboats provided by the Dock Board, the steam tug companies maintained their own. A disaster in which ten men were lost from one of these lifeboats occurred in 1854. The barque *Cherokee* of 265 tons had sailed from Liverpool on Friday 17 February 1854 for Africa with general cargo. A severe NW gale, with gusts close to hurricane strength, blew up and she was driven ashore on the East Hoyle Bank at 9am on the next morning. Two tugs set off to her rescue with lifeboats in tow. Early on Saturday morning, the Steam Tug Company's *President* took the Liverpool lifeboat in tow via the Victoria channel. They were unable to approach the wreck because of heavy surf. Meanwhile, at about 11am, the steam tug *Victoria* took her company's lifeboat in tow. This lifeboat was crewed by 10 men who were river boatmen and was commanded by Captain William Roberts of the tug *Albert* who had volunteered for this rescue mission. They proceeded out through the Rock Channel. A huge wave struck the lifeboat and it capsized. The men on the tug tried to rescue them but only one man was brought to safety. The lifeboat was a well tried boat which had saved many and the crew had full confidence in her. The crew on the *Cherokee* got off, some in their own boat, some with help from the Hoylake lifeboat. The *Cherokee* drifted off the Bank at high tide and came ashore at Dove Point. She was upright and not leaking so that she was put back into service. No lives were lost from her crew of 17 but 10 lives were lost in the upsetting of the Steam Tug Company's lifeboat.

A lifeboat disaster had occurred much earlier, on 13 January 1836, when Lt. Joseph Walker, RN, keeper of Formby Lighthouse, and four of the Formby lifeboat's crew were drowned. Lt.Walker saw a schooner with damaged sails among the breakers off Mad Wharf. He fired the gun to summon the lifeboat crew and they dragged the boat three miles to the sea's edge near the wreck by 4pm. They rowed out to the *Bryades* but found no one aboard. As they returned to the beach, the lifeboat broached in surf and capsized. Three of eight men aboard were under the upturned boat. One, Edward Alty, managed to get out from underneath and climb on the hull. He considered himself the only survivor when the boat was washed ashore. On the shore, people heard noises under the boat, lifted her up, and two men crawled out. They had survived by keeping their heads above water by holding onto cross-members and breathing the air trapped under the boat. So three out of 8 gallant men survived. Yet again, not one of the crew was wearing a lifebelt.

Ironically, in each of these three cases, the lifeboat rescue mission was actually in vain, since the vessel in distress had either already been assisted by another lifeboat, or the crew had got away in their own ship's boat. It is especially tragic when brave men are lost in a futile endeavour.

A memorable and heroic lifesaving act had occurred a few years earlier. The Liverpool Pilot Boat No. 1 *Good Intent* with 21 pilots and crew aboard was caught in a great storm on the night of 19 to 20 November 1833. A huge wave washed her boarding punt off her deck and into the sail which was torn. The wind ripped the damaged sail to shreds and she became unmanageable. She was driven onto an offshore sandbank a mile or two north of the Formby lifeboat house. The tide was high and the waves beating against the door of the boat house caused a delay in getting the lifeboat out. When the lifeboat was launched, the lifeboatmen could not cross the sandbank to get close to the wrecked vessel to help the crew who were seen clinging to the rigging. Meanwhile two lifeboatmen who had not gone out in the lifeboat found the Pilot Boat's punt which had been washed onto the beach. They righted it and set off to the wreck. Someone on the lifeboat saw the body of a man floating near the wreck and called out to Dr. Sumner, the village surgeon, to give assistance. Richard Sumner was not a member of the lifeboat crew but had accompanied them previously to assist in the recovery of shipwrecked men. Dr. Sumner who was 35, plunged into the surf and reached the lifeboat. Using the punt, two crew members and Dr. Sumner managed to get to the wreck and take off some of the crew and bring them ashore. The surgeon had taken the precaution of sending a lad for a bottle of rum and this was used as a restorative to the rescued men who were at the limit of their endurance. Of the crew of 21, only 9 were saved. Dr. Sumner had shown great courage and initiative in very difficult circumstances. He was awarded two gold medals - by the Royal Humane Society and by the Shipwreck Institution. Such an award of a double gold medal was very rare - it was more than Grace Darling and her father were to be awarded five years later for their much better known rescue attempt.

As well as the heroic efforts of the lifeboat crews, an insight into the dangers of sea travel in the 1860s comes from the record of shipping disasters. The Liverpool newspapers listed shipwrecks, somewhere in the world, every day. Even close to Liverpool, because of the huge volume of shipping coming in and out, accidents were inevitable. The annual Board of Trade report listed the shipwrecks and loss of life, for example 340 lives were lost in 1858 around the coast of Britain, while 1645 lives were lost in 1859, because of a severe gale which affected the West Coast.

The biggest disaster in recent memory was that of the 2717 ton steam clipper *Royal Charter*. She was inbound to Liverpool from Melbourne with many passengers including returning gold miners. The weather on the night of 25 October 1859 was exceptionally bad and many vessels were lost around the coast of Britain. The *Royal Charter* anchored off the East coast of Anglesey but was driven onto the rocky coast by the force of the storm. Of the 371 passengers and 112 crew aboard, only 21 passengers and 18 crew survived: 16 by climbing along a rope hawser and 23 who were washed or swam ashore. No women or children were among those who reached safety. Many of the passengers had valuable gold in bags and belts and this weight reduced any chance they had of getting ashore alive. The remaining wreckage is just north of Moelfre, and is visited by divers.

On 3 December 1863, a severe gale caused widespread damage to shipping. The port surveyor went out in a tug the next day to check that the buoys marking the channel were still in place, and he reported finding 12 wrecks in Liverpool Bay and another two in Hilbre Swash. The lifeboats were kept busy: Southport lifeboat rescued the crew of the *Dewitt Clinton*, inbound from Boston with timber, which grounded at Formby Point; the Point of Ayr lifeboat went out to help a stranded schooner; the Hoylake lifeboat rescued the four crew of the schooner *George* who had taken to her rigging when she grounded on West Hoyle Bank; the Liverpool No. 1 lifeboat rescued the crew of the *Pensacola* of 1420 tons burden, also carrying timber from North America, taking off 15 men, although the captain and three men stayed aboard to try to refloat her off Burbo Bank. This proved impractical and they were later taken off by a boat from the Liverpool Limited Steam Company. Some were less lucky, the inbound schooner *Mary* of Montrose picked up a pilot, plus two more pilots who wanted to return to Liverpool. She was lost with all hands, including the three Liverpool pilots.

An unusual disaster occurred in the Mersey itself, off Liverpool, on 15 January 1864. The barque *Lottie Sleigh*, carrying a cargo of 11 tons of gunpowder, was at anchor mid-river near the Laird shipbuilding yard. On board at 6pm the steward was trimming a paraffin lamp on the cabin table when he spilled some of the paraffin which caught fire. The bed curtains ignited and, as the fire spread, it got closer to where the gunpowder was stored. The crew urgently hailed the Rock Ferry steamer *Wasp* and, on jumping aboard, they urged her captain to get clear as fast as possible. They were lucky to escape with their lives, for the *Lottie Sleigh* exploded 3 minutes later. This explosion was very violent and glass was broken in many buildings ashore. The noise was tremendous and was heard as far

*The explosion of the Lottie Sleigh,
seen from Birkenhead*

away as Chester - some 20 miles. Her deck gun was blown over two miles onto New Brighton sands. Part of her hull was blown 5 miles to Eastham. Amazingly, nobody was injured. The issue of whether the Royal Insurance Company could make ex-gratia payments for the damaged windows under Fire policies was decided in a court case. Because of this link, Royal Insurance bought the figurehead of the *Lottie Sleigh* and later they presented it to the Merseyside Maritime Museum where it is now on display.

Another accident which, thankfully, was without loss of life, occurred on 3 October 1864 when the big trans-atlantic Royal Mail passenger steamship *Jura* inbound from Quebec lost her way in the shipping channel and grounded off Crosby. As the tide ebbed, she broke her back and had to be abandoned for scrap. Her imposing wreck would have been a reminder to ships navigating the shipping channel of the need for vigilance. As recently as 1995, a part of her boiler could still be seen at the water's edge on a very low tide.

The approach by sea to Liverpool from Point Lynas on Anglesey is only 40 miles and many ships considered themselves 'home' when they passed Anglesey inbound. Commander Denham RN surveyed Liverpool Bay in the 1840s and he wrote in his sailing directions 'Little does the merchant think in his calculations, when stopping the insurance on learning his cargo is off Point Lynas; why 'tis then the risk commences.'

Chapter 6
Liverpool in late 1864

In Liverpool there was great interest in the fate of blockade runners and the newspapers carried reports every few days, as news came in from either the Union or Confederate side. The shortage of cotton imports from the South was having a serious effect on the Lancashire cotton mills, with much hardship among the workers. The news of success or failure of particular ships was tinged with self interest, since many Liverpool businessmen had invested in blockade running. There were also offices of shipping agents with strong links to the Confederacy. Many of the blockade runners had been built on the Mersey and their crews were often from Liverpool too.

News of blockade runners included the bad news that the big Liverpool-built *Hope* had been captured on 22 October 1864. As well as the loss of the *Mary Celestia* in Bermuda, other Liverpool-built blockade runners lost from September to November 1864 were the *Badger, Lynx, Lucy* and *Bat*. This left the *Fox* and *Owl* built by Jones Quiggin, and the *Let her B/Chicora* built by Millers, as the only Liverpool-built runners still getting through on the Atlantic coast at that date. Clearly the business of running the blockade was becoming very risky. Although 6 vessels were lost, many more were under construction on the Mersey. Another large steel blockade runner, *Colonel Lamb*, had a successful trial in the Mersey on 13 October. She was commanded by the experienced Captain Thomas Lockwood and was later reported to have arrived in Nassau via Halifax. She made a successful run into Wilmington on 29 November 1864.

Some idea of the widespread support for the Confederate cause in Liverpool can be gauged from the success of the Confederate Bazaar. This was held in St. George's Hall, then located in Derby Square, over four days from 18-22 October. In was in aid of the Southern Prisoner's Relief Fund and very many well-known Liverpool names supported and patronised it. From ticket sales and from selling off donated items, over £20,000 was raised. This large sum was not used to alleviate the suffering of Southern prisoners, its intended purpose, because permission was witheld by the Union authorities.

Another example of sentiment in Liverpool was the newspaper reports in early November of the seizure by a Union warship of the CSS *Florida* in neutral Bahia - which was described as 'dastardly conduct'. The Miller-built CSS *Florida* was captured by the USS *Wachusett* while at anchor in a neutral port, Bahia in Brazil. She was then towed to Hampton Roads - the Brazilian navy was unable to halt this illegal action. Diplomatic pressure required the *Florida* to be returned to the Brazilian government, which would restore her to the Confederacy. Instead she 'accidentally' sank in Hampton Roads. The Union navy officers in charge were publicly chastised, and one year later given a promotion retroactive to the date of the sinking. The captured crew of the *Florida*, including Arthur Sinclair's son Terry Sinclair(jr), were imprisoned, but then released when the illegality of their capture was admitted. They were directed to travel to Liverpool.

Other news coming in about the conflict was that a new commerce raider, the CSS *Shenandoah*, was being equipped in Madeira; that the yellow fever epidemic at Bermuda had subsided and that Union forces were building up off Wilmington. The key to running the blockade into Wilmington was Fort Fisher which provided covering fire for the entrance to the Cape Fear River. News reached Liverpool in early January that a major Union attempt to take Fort Fisher on Christmas Eve had been repulsed by Confederate Forces. It was expected that the Union forces would regroup and attack again. Although the Confederates still controlled the access to Wilmington, it was likely that a more determined Union attack would soon prevail. This made it even more imperative that every Confederate resource was brought to bear as soon as possible.

The Mersey shipyards were working flat out building blockade runners and Miller's yard was full. Millers were building three large capacity steel vessels, to the same design, intended as blockade runners. The nearest to completion had been ordered by William Crenshaw & Co. She was launched and towed into dock to have her engines installed and her fitting out completed. Two more sister ships, later to be named *Abigail* and *Ray*, had been ordered by Fraser Trentholm and were in a less advanced state of construction.

Although blockade runners were sailed from Liverpool as British-registered vessels with captain and crew having Board of Trade certificates, it was becoming usual to have aboard not just the delivery captain but also the confederate leader who would run the blockade, so that no time was lost on arrival in Bermuda or Nassau. Arthur Sinclair with his engineer Charles Middleton had been ordered to Liverpool for just this reason, to be ready to sail when their designated vessel was ready.

Because of his experience aboard the *Mary Celestia*, a blockade runner built by Millers and owned by Crenshaws who had a contract to deliver much needed supplies to the Confederacy, he was assigned to the ship that Millers were completing for Crenshaws. As an honour, the ship was named *Lelia*, after his wife Lelia Imogen (née Dawley). He must have been very proud, looking forward to being in command of one of the latest design of blockade runners, named after his wife.

The name 'Lelia' was unusual but, by coincidence, another ship had been registered with that name at Liverpool in 1864. The usual pronunciation is to rhyme with 'Celia' and 'Delia'. Confusingly, 'Leila' is also a girl's name.

The *Lelia* was ready for her sea trial on 6 January 1865. Aboard were Arthur Sinclair, Thomas Miller and Thomas Miller's brother-in-law Captain James Duguid. Both Arthur Sinclair and James Duguid had recent experience running the blockade, aboard *Mary Celestia* and *Lucy* respectively. They would have been able to assess *Lelia's* potential for blockade running.

The local newspaper reported the trial: "The new steamship *Lelia* left the North Landing Stage on yesterday morning on a trial trip, with a select company of ladies and gentlemen. The steamer has been built by Messrs. W.C. Miller and Sons, and is, we are given to understand, intended for the West India trade. The *Lelia* is a paddlewheel steamer of 1,100 tons. Her length is 265 feet, breadth 30 feet, and depth 15 feet. She is fitted with engines of 300-horse power nominal, constructed by Messrs. Fawcett, Preston, and Co., and her paddles are constructed on the patent feathering principle. The ship left the Landing-stage at half-past ten o'clock, and proceeded on a cruise up and down the river. After sailing up the river as far as the Sloyne her head was turned, and she reached the Rock Lighthouse at 11 46 a.m., and the North-West lightship at 12:39 p.m. After steaming round the North-West Lightship, she returned with the flood tide, leaving the lightship at one o'clock and reaching the Rock Lighthouse at 1 47 p.m. The distance from the North-west Lightship to the Rock is 14 miles, The *Lelia*, with 400 tons of dead weight on board, ran the measured mile in 3 minutes 20 seconds, and her average speed during the trip was about 18 miles

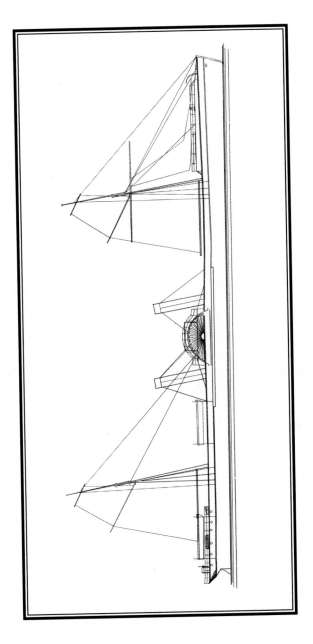

The rigging plan of the Lelia

Lelia

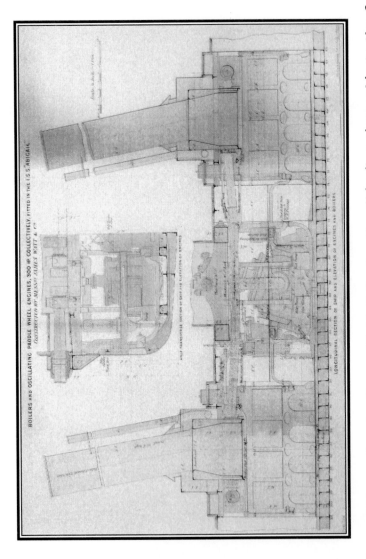

Plans of the engines by James Watt & Co. for the Abigail, a sister ship to the Lelia

A reconstruction of the appearance of the Lelia at sea.

per hour. Her engines indicated 1950-horse power, the pressure of steam being 35 lbs. to the square inch. The revolutions were 36 per minute."

This was a very impressive performance. The *Lelia* was one of the fastest ships afloat. She was insured for £32,000 which compares with the cost of building the larger *Colonel Lamb* of £50,000 for which it was said that no expense had been spared.

Lelia was registered at Liverpool as a British vessel on 10 January 1865, the details are given in an appendix. She was described as a steel paddle steamer owned by Henry Elias Moss of Rumford Place, Liverpool. Even though Crenshaws were the managers of the *Lelia*, it was prudent to arrange that she was formally owned by a Briton, the Liverpool shipbroker Henry Elias Moss. Her designated captain, Thomas Buxton Skinner, was a native of Virginia, then aged 38, who had been involved in the regular merchant shipping trade between Liverpool and the Southern USA before the Civil War. Thus she was British owned and registered and had a crew certified by the British Board of Trade. This avoided any prospect that Union spies could claim that she was going to be used to aid the Confederate War effort. Crenshaws acted openly as managers from their offices in Borough Buildings North and in Rumford Street, hiring the crew and ordering the supplies to be put aboard.

The *Lelia* had steel frames and hull plates, but her stern and stem (and possibly her keel) would have been of iron since that could be built into complex shapes more easily. The hurricane deck, more commonly known as a turtle-back, was a covering of the bow area, designed to stop waves from breaking onto the main deck. It had hatches that could be opened to get the anchors inboard and the crew accommodation was built on the main deck underneath it. The accommodation for the officers and passengers was astern, under the raised poop deck. The cabins here were said to be very grand. *Lelia* had two masts and two funnels. The engines were amidships with bunkers to hold coal fore and aft. She had two holds with hatches to each and patent steam winches to aid loading and unloading. Between the two paddle wheels was a bridge which had a small pilot house. She could be steered from this pilot house or from a wheel at the stern. Most ships have rails around the main deck, but blockade runners had substantial steel bulwarks - 4.5 ft high in the case of *Lelia* - which gave the crew protection from gunfire when running the blockade. *Lelia* had powerful engines which needed almost 50 tons of coal a day at full speed. With her coal bunker capacity of 340 tons, this gave her enough range to steam from Bermuda to Wilmington and back. Crossing the Atlantic, she would have relied on sail, except when speed was needed to avoid any Union warship.

Arthur Sinclair, in conjunction with Crenshaws and James Bulloch, would have ordered the stores and cargo to be put aboard the *Lelia*. She had already taken aboard coal for her engines before her trial. The remainder of her cargo was stowed in the following days. As well as the bunkers which would be filled with coal, a substantial amount of coal was also stowed in the fore and aft holds. This would give her more capability for blockade running after reaching Bermuda.

Union spies were observing the *Lelia* carefully, looking for any possibility that she could be prevented from sailing for breaking neutrality and also noting an accurate description of her appearance so she might be identified by the blockading force. There were reports on 11 and 14 January to the Union consul in Liverpool which he passed on to Washington (see appendix). One of these describes the cargo being loaded as 'steel in bars, lead, boiler plates, army spades, casks supposed to contain shot, etc'. Their reports also describe her appearance and colour: grey hull, black funnels and white ship's boats. A later Union spy reported the loading of a 2 cwt case directed to Mr McLeish Bermuda, 20 casks of iron, baskets of potatoes, onions and other vegetables. These same Union spies reported that *Lelia* was suitable for 'piratical' purposes since she was strongly built, meaning that guns could be mounted aboard to give her an offensive role. This was a real possibility: in late 1864 two blockade runners had been fitted with a few guns each at Wilmington, renamed CSS *Olustee* and CSS *Chickamauga*, and sailed up the North American coast as commerce raiders.

The ship was not full, either in the fore or aft hold, having on board 85 tons of cargo and 460 tons of coal for ship's use. As specified by the design of the *Lelia*, she was loaded so that the main deck was 2.5 ft above sea level amidships. This meant that wave crests would be above deck level, even in moderate seas, and there would be a lot of water coming on deck. By modern standards this would be unacceptable, but blockade runners were designed to lie low in the water to avoid detection. Vessels of similar design had previously crossed the Atlantic without problems.

Hugh Gould, surveyor of Customs at Liverpool, cleared *Lelia* to put to sea. Her papers, which consisted of the manifest, contents and victualling bill, showed what she had declared as cargo, principally hardware and machinery. Although the Confederate cause would have been best served by arms and ammunition, Union spies would have reported any such cargo and a court case would have delayed her departure. It is possible that some specialised equipment such as electric cables, batteries etc were put on board, intended for use in submarine warfare, as was the case when *Owl* had carried 10 miles of insulated wire and two 'exploders' when she left Liverpool on her maiden voyage on 29 July 1864. Both Miller and the confederates would have been very much relieved that *Lelia* was cleared for sea, after so many previous occasions where delays had occurred. The materials on board, iron and lead, could indeed be turned into ammunition on arrival. Spades were also needed by the army. These items were not explicitly for military use, so escaped censure.

The *Leila* took on board her final stores and crew in the Carriers Dock which was the northernmost dock at Liverpool at that date. Thomas Miller instructed their foreman shipwright, James Forfar, to deliver the small stores to the *Lelia*: these were small metal and wooden items, rowlocks, keys, blocks to close the hawse pipes, etc. The foreman intended to deliver them to the ship's carpenter, but since the carpenter was the worse for drink, he left them with the first mate, Lauritz Jonas Peterson, originally from Copenhagen. He also showed the mate how the patent steam windlass worked.

The crew was quite a multi-national band. There were Scandinavians and Canadians as well as a number from the Southern United States, including her certified skipper Thomas Buxton Skinner of Virginia. One of the firemen, Peter Laverty, had been a fireman aboard the CSS *Alabama* and had survived her sinking off Cherbourg.

As well as the certified crew, she carried passengers. These were not passengers in the sense of paying passengers but men associated with shipbuilding, with trade and men returning to help the confederate cause. Foremost among them was Arthur Sinclair who was to take over command when she reached Bermuda. His chief engineer, Charles Middleton, was also aboard but was listed as crew. Some of those aboard were intending to travel only as far as Holyhead. Thomas Miller, as a representative of the shipyard who built the *Lelia*, was aboard to check out her performance at sea when fully laden, this was common practice on a maiden voyage.

The Liverpool pilot, William Williams and a clerk with Crenshaw's named James Clark were also to leave at Holyhead. William Williams had served in the pilot service with some distinction for about thirty years and had recently been promoted to 3rd master of the No.1 Pilot Boat. He was one of those from the pilot boat who had volunteered to go aboard at great risk to help the crew of the *Providence* when she was dismasted in a severe gale.

The planned route included a stop at Cork on the way and a Cork-based pilot, Magnus Park, who had brought a vessel into Liverpool, was aboard returning home. The remaining men going to Bermuda were John Cropper and C.L. Hobson (shipping agents), Messrs Gerchart and Campbell and the gunner from the CSS *Alabama*, Thomas C. Cuddy. It was also likely that a stop would be made in Madeira, to replenish her coal bunkers.

Chapter 7

The maiden voyage

A maiden voyage is a time for celebration with the excitement of making a first trip in a brand new and purpose-built vessel. *Lelia's* intended purpose of running the blockade was known to involve danger, but the delivery trip to Bermuda was expected to be uneventful and a chance for her eventual captain, Arthur Sinclair, to get to know the vessel better.

A commander in the confederate navy received an annual salary of $2,400 (about £500) while at sea. Arthur Sinclair, however, had made significant profits while blockade running from Bermuda to Wilmington. He was carrying a letter of credit from Crenshaw & Co, for £1,300, and he had prudently left instructions as to how this was to be distributed to his family should he be lost. He had a newly bought gold watch made by Robert Roskell of Liverpool which had cost £40, a large sum in those days. The watch chain with mariner's gold compass and a gold locket, containing a plait of his wife Lelia's hair, was a gift to Sinclair from Mr. C. L. Hobson, a fellow passenger and a manager with Crenshaw and Company, the vessel's eventual owners. Because of the value of the watch, friends in Liverpool had urged him to leave it behind when he went to sea, but he explained that if he was wrecked on the coast while blockade running, he could use it to procure food and shelter. He was smartly

Some of those on board the Lelia: Commander Arthur Sinclair (standing) and Thomas C. Cuddy (gunner on the Alabama)

dressed in warm clothes and, with a black satin cravat with a gold and agate pin, he was an imposing sight. At 54 years of age, he needed steel-rimmed spectacles for reading which he kept in a leather case.

Arthur Sinclair was host to the passengers aboard. They would have been very impressed by the facilities and accommodation, the cabin aft was furnished in a grand manner and there were 3 cooks and 5 stewards to look after the officers and passengers. He would have been able to impress the passengers with his wide experience: cruising the Pacific Ocean, building ironclad warships and blockade running in the *Mary Celestia*. Thomas Miller, though much younger at 28 years old, represented one of the world leaders in steel shipbuilding. Millers had built the CSS *Florida* and blockade runners such as the pioneering steel *Phantom* and the very successful *Let her B*. He was looking forward to confirming the excellent performance that the *Lelia* had shown on her trials. Also aboard was Thomas Cuddy, gunner aboard the very successful commerce raider CSS *Alabama*, who would have been able to provide first hand accounts of many daring exploits.

The weather on the morning of Saturday 14th January 1865 was unsettled. The barometer gave one of the lowest readings for many years, indicating that a severe storm system was passing. No storm signal was hoisted at Liverpool and the wind was moderate. *Lelia* was to cross the Atlantic in winter, so she could expect gales sooner or later. As well as the ominous weather, another reason to delay was that the ship's equipment had not yet been fully stowed in its correct place. There were also strong arguments for leaving as soon as possible: to avoid any possible Union inspired legal delay; to bring help to the Confederate cause as soon as possible. From the viewpoint of the shipbuilders who were not pro-confederate but businessmen, they would have been anxious to deliver the ship and receive payment, especially as there were indications that blockade running might soon become infeasible.

The decision was taken by Captain Skinner and Commander Sinclair to set out. Only three vessels left Liverpool that morning, one being the big iron Cunard mailboat SS *Cuba*, bound for the USA.

Under the command of Captain Thomas Buxton Skinner and the Liverpool pilot Williams Williams, *Lelia* left her anchorage off Rock Ferry on the last of the flood tide at about 9 am, proceeding at full speed. The wind had picked up to a strong breeze from the NW. Passing the Formby Lightship she was slowed so that the port anchor, which had been left outboard in case they needed to re-anchor, could be brought inboard. The seas were building up and the second mate was swept from the hurricane deck onto the main deck by a big wave breaking over her bow as he was stowing the anchor. Both anchors were stowed with the fluke over the rail and the crown on the deck which meant that the hatches at the forward end of the

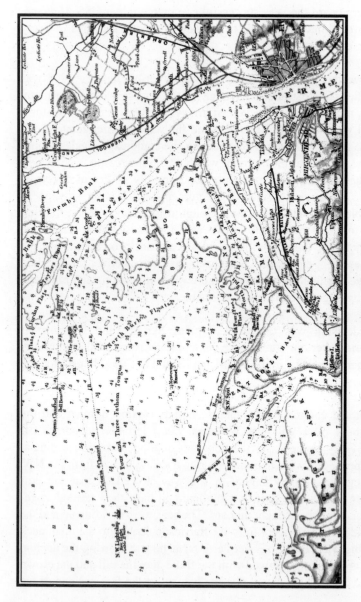

A chart of Liverpool Bay in 1864. Liverpool is at the bottom right.

hurricane deck for retrieving the anchors could not be closed. They continued at full speed and reached the Bell Buoy by midday. As *Lelia* left the shelter of the shipping channel, the seas got much worse. With the tide now ebbing strongly, the current was against the NW wind, making short steep waves which broke over her bows as she headed straight into them. It was cold with some sleet. The strain on her hull and structure was very great as she crashed into the oncoming waves. The men steering her from the bridge noticed that the guard rail had become distorted by the flexing of the ship.

As each steep wave broke over her bow, water was getting aboard, both through the open anchor hatches and also up through the hawse pipes (pipes from outside of the hull to the foredeck for the anchor chain to run through). The crew could not find the blocking fitments for the hawse pipes so they stuffed blankets and pillows in them. Water was coming on deck faster than it could drain off and the weight of water on deck smashed the wooden bulkhead of the crew accommodation which was on the main deck under the hurricane deck. Their clothes, berths and bedding were washed out of the deckhouse and overboard.

Provided the main deck stayed watertight, the water surging around on it would be an inconvenience, ruining the crew's accommodation, but would not sink the ship. Men were sent forward to check that the main deck was still watertight. The volume of water on deck, and the amount of debris being swept around by it, made this a dangerous activity and also made it impossible to be sure that water wasn't getting below. Reports suggested that some water could be getting below deck either through the forepeak scuttle, or from some damage to the deck caused by the anchor crown stowed on it. The pumps were got ready, the pumps aft of the engines were worked by the donkey engine but there was no water to pump out aft of the engines. To connect up the steam pump to the fore part, a key was needed to turn on the sluice valves. The carpenter could not find the key, saying he had never received it. Some water on the foredeck was also getting below through the fore stoke-hold grating, which lets air into the engines, and the men tried to block this with bedding.

The weight of water shipped caused *Lelia* to settle down by the head. With her bows lower in the water, she was even more vulnerable to waves breaking over the bow. The pilot called Captain Skinner and recommended that the engines were slowed. The captain asked what it would be best to do, and the pilot said he thought she would reach Holyhead. The ship did not pitch into the sea so much when she was going slower. Captain Skinner told the pilot that he thought it would be better to turn back. While they were discussing their options, she shipped a very heavy sea which shook her all over, and then the pilot told the helmsman to put the helm to starboard. The pilot also ordered the crew to get the four ship's boats ready and they were lowered ready to leave. She would not turn with her helm hard to starboard, so the pilot ordered the wheel hard to port instead. To help turn her, the foretopmast staysail was hoisted. She only turned partly to port and then stopped. Orders were then given to set the fore and aft foresails. With this extra canvas the wind swung her head round and she was put on full speed running before the wind back to Liverpool. Arthur Sinclair came on deck and ordered the boats to be hoisted up again, as, he said, the ship was all right. They were hoisted up and secured.

The crew were exhausted and wet from the buffeting they received from the water trapped on the foredeck. As was usual in those days, grog was served out twice to refresh the men.

The decision to return had been taken when they were passing Great Orme's Head. Running downwind the ship was more manageable. She still buried her head into waves and her bow was so low in the water that seas still came aboard. She was difficult to steer from amidships so the stern wheel was connected and used. The men pumping on the deck still had to contend with being knocked over by the water surging around them. Moreover, the pumps delivered the water on deck, where it added to the problem. The engineer ordered the carpenter to take a sledge hammer to knock a plate out of the bulwarks, to let the water escape more easily from the foredeck. Because of the quantity of water on the deck, the carpenter was unable to do this. Soon afterwards he was washed overboard.

She kept her course easily when steered from the aft wheel for about an hour and a half, during which time, they were making about 7.5 knots, the tide being against her. The foresail had been taken down. When they turned back to Liverpool, a signal of distress was made by hoisting their ensign upside down. They had two small guns on board, but these were not used for signalling. An outward bound steamer, the *Sovereign* of Bristol, turned to follow them for some distance. Since the *Lelia* was making a fair speed, the *Sovereign* was not able to catch up, so seeing that they did not slow down, she went back to her original course. The *Lelia's* pilot and captain may have thought that the *Sovereign* had decided to return to Liverpool, rather than offer assistance. When they saw the *Sovereign* revert to her original course, they realised that she had been ready to help. The *Lelia* was slowed and oilcloth coats were hung up in the rigging as additional signals of distress. It was too late, the *Sovereign* was heading away from them.

The wind was still increasing in strength and the waves became higher and higher. A big wave caught her stern port quarter and pushed her round until she was lying broadside to the waves. Her foretopmast staysail was ripped to shreds by the force of the wind. After some fifteen minutes lying across the waves, the foresail was set again and her head was turned downwind. She was difficult to steer, with the force of the waves on the rudder causing the wheel to react violently, beyond the control of the helmsmen. The wind and waves forced her to head more upwind until they were abreast of the N.W. Lightship, and about four or five miles from it.

Yet again she buried her head into a wave and the wind drove her stern around so that she lay across the waves. She would not respond to the wheel and the engines were reversed at full speed to see if she could be headed downwind again but, even though the foresail was still set, she would not turn. Then she rolled very heavily, quivered alarmingly, shipped a very heavy sea, and the fore hatches burst open. They burst open from below from the pressure of water and air in the forehold. The water on the foredeck was level with the combings of the hatch, 'and every time the ship rolled more water went down below. The crew were then all aft, the main deck forward being level with the sea.

It must have been a shock to the passengers to realise that the comfort of their surroundings was illusory. The *Lelia* was not going to take them to safety, they would have to take to her boats. Conditions were very bad. The *Lelia* was wallowing in huge waves and it was cold and nearly dark. The captain gave orders to lower the boats and the starboard waist boat on the lee was lowered first. The two pilots got in, followed by some of the passengers, including Arthur Sinclair, and many of the crew, so that there were about fifteen people in the boat. Captain Skinner went down into the boat to place the people in her and then climbed back on deck and gave orders for the next boat to be lowered. As *Lelia* rolled and was pushed downwind, the sponson (side projection around the paddle wheel) hit the starboard boat and sank it. None of the men in that boat survived. The smaller port waist lifeboat was lowered next, too many got into her, the aft davit was bent down to the water and the boat half filled. The second steward fell overboard and was pulled back in by a fireman. The tackle was cut by one of the firemen who was in her and the boat drifted clear. There were ten firemen, one seaman, and the second steward in this smaller boat. The port quarter boat was then lowered safely into the water with seventeen men in her, including Thomas Miller. Captain Skinner came to the wheel and ordered the helmsmen, Brodie and Currie, to abandon

The Lelia in heavy weather

ship. Brodie went down the tackle and got into that boat on the port side. He said to Captain Skinner before he left the deck, "Captain Skinner, are you going in this boat" and he replied "Yes Brodie, go down and I'll follow you." As soon as Brodie got into the boat, the tackle was let go, and they pulled round the stern to the starboard side of the ship. When they got there they saw Captain Skinner and Currie trying to free the starboard quarter boat which was hanging from the aft tackle with the forward tackle released, so that it was swamped by water. They could not see clearly what had happened to the men assigned to that boat and they could not get near Captain Skinner and Currie to give them any assistance.

When the survivors, including Thomas Miller, had got into the larger port quarter boat, they found that it was not provided with the necessary equipment, although there were oars aboard. There were no rowlocks, so they improvised by breaking up the boat hook to make some thole pins which could be slotted into holes in the gunwale and so give support to an oar. As well as these improvised rowlocks, they also assigned one man to hold an oar near the gunwale while another rowed with it. The rudder of the boat was inadequately secured and was washed away soon after they left the *Lelia*, so they had to steer with oars. They were heading down wind with following waves, so they needed to pull on the oars to keep clear of any waves that might break over them. The mate wanted to head for shore but Thomas Miller said that the breakers on shore would be too violent and ordered them to head for the N.W. Lightship which was just visible downwind. Three rockets were seen to go up from the *Lelia*, a signal of distress from Captain Skinner and Currie. In an open boat in huge waves and gale force wind, Thomas Miller's group of survivors were far from safe themselves. The lack of proper rowlocks or rudder gave them very limited control over where they went. As they approached the lightship, they passed the smaller boat from the port waist of the *Lelia* which had set off earlier, also making for the lightship. Men on that boat had hoisted an oar to act as a sail and were steering with another oar. This gives an idea of the strength of the wind which was at its strongest at that time.

At 5.45 pm as light faded, the larger boat got alongside the lightship and three lines were thrown to them. The first mate got hold of one of the lines and tied it around the midship thwart, which brought the boat broadside on to the stern of the lightship. A big wave then struck the boat and capsized her, turning her keel up, and all eighteen men were thrown into the water. Thomas Miller had been helping to row all the time, and he and Brodie were under the lee side of the boat. They got out from underneath and swam to the lightship. Brodie got hold of one of the lines and started to climb up the line when the mate caught hold of him by the leg and pulled him back into the water. Thomas Miller had got hold of a thin line but then grabbed the same line as Brodie. With three men, Thomas Miller, Brodie and the mate on the same line, the lightship crew were unable to haul all three men up together and were obliged to slacken off the rope. When the rope was released, the mate let go of Brodie's leg and was not seen again. Thomas Miller was still holding on to the rope with one hand and to Brodie's coat with the other hand. A circular lifebuoy was thrown over, and Brodie got inside it. Since his hands were numb from the cold, he put his arms over the buoy and said "Miller, you can hold on by me now, for you cannot pull me out of the life buoy." The men on board the lightship attempted to reeve the line through the vang block, and they again loosened the line, so that both Thomas Miller and Brodie went under water. When Brodie came up Thomas Miller was gone. Brodie was then hauled on board. There were only three others saved from that boat: Smith (the boatswain), Scott, and Obey. Smith and Obey had managed to get onto the keel of the boat as it capsized.

The smaller boat then arrived and, in their haste to be saved, three of the cooks jumped overboard to get hold of the line that was hanging over the side of the lightship, but in the icy water they were unable to hold on and all three drowned. The boat was secured alongside the lightship and most of the men were pulled safely on board the lightship by the lightship crew under Captain Roberts. Smith and Obey, who had been on the keel of the upturned larger boat, managed to swim to the smaller boat and were helped aboard.

The lightship crew did all they could for the exhausted sailors they had pulled on board. They gave them clothes, warm drinks and bunks to lie on, sleeping on the deck floor themselves.

Chapter 8

The Liverpool lifeboat

Captain John Parry was used to rough weather. His ship, the steam tug *Blazer* of the Liverpool Steam Tug Company, was in her element patrolling the seas off the Liverpool Bar. A typical day would involve locating an incoming sailing ship and negotiating a deal to tow her into Liverpool. Sunday 15th January 1865 was not to be a typical day.

Blazer was a 150 ft long paddle tug, built in Glasgow in 1856, with engines of 150 nhp. Paddle wheels were favoured for tugs since each wheel could be controlled individually, giving the tug an excellent ability to manoeuvre. Miller's was one of the Liverpool shipyards specialising in tugs, having recently built the *Emperor* in 1863 and the *Knight Templar* in 1864.

Passing the Northwest Lightship, Captain Parry saw that there was a distress signal hoisted. He brought his vessel close alongside so that he could be hailed by the master of the Lightship. Captain Roberts informed him that they had survivors from the shipwreck of the *Leila* aboard and that they should be taken into Liverpool. The northwest gale-force winds had abated a little from the previous day, but since the waves were still very high, it was difficult to bring the tug close alongside the anchored lightvessel without risk of collision. After a few attempts, Captain Parry was convinced that he could not pick up the survivors safely without endangering his own vessel. He knew that assistance could be provided using a lighter well-fendered boat that could be brought alongside the Lightship safely in the heavy seas. What was needed was a lifeboat: and Liverpool led the world in the provision of lifeboats.

In 1865, the Mersey Docks and Harbour Board provided seven lifeboats with permanent crews, two being kept afloat near the Liverpool Landing stage. To speed up rescue, an arrangement existed with the tug companies that as soon as a signal of distress was received, one of their tugs would proceed immediately and take the first available lifeboat in tow. Although the reward for towing out a lifeboat was relatively small (£15), the masters of the steam tugs were very willing to perform this service and jealous should a rival tug try to assist. The honour of assisting in life-saving in dreadful weather was one that brought credit to them, their vessel and their company.

Captain Parry proceeded at full speed to the Liverpool Landing stage to seek help, arriving at 13.15. There were two lifeboats kept at the Prince's Landing stage at the heart of Liverpool: the Liverpool No 1 lifeboat had been built to the tried and tested Liverpool design by a local builder, Thomas Costain, in 1839, and was 30 ft long with 9.25 ft beam with some built-in buoyancy, pulled by 10 oars; the Liverpool No 2 boat was built to a newer design favoured by the RNLI and was described as self-righting. The lifeboatmen actually preferred the older design since it was more stable under most conditions, even though there had been previous occasions when similar boats had capsized.

It was actually the turn of No 2 lifeboat to go out but since her crew was not ready in time, No 1 was chosen. Some of the crew of No 2 took places aboard and an old boatman called Ward had taken a seat when he was called away on an errand, his place being taken by another volunteer. He had narrowly missed joining the crew of the Steam Tug Co's lifeboat some years ago, so avoiding the disaster when that lifeboat capsized under tow, losing twelve of her crew of thirteen. The No 1 lifeboat was ready in 15 minutes, under the command of her master Thomas Hudson, to be towed out with a crew of ten men coming from both lifeboats plus three volunteers: George Hampson, James Martindale and James Bannin. The weather conditions were bad, but they had been out in such conditions before, so the lifeboatmen were not expecting trouble - rather a routine trip to pick up the survivors of the *Lelia* from the Northwest Lightship.

The lifeboatmen were provided with cork-filled lifebelts and the rules stated "The lifebelts to be worn at all occasions of duty afloat. The master is not to permit a boat to be taken in tow until every man has put on his lifebelt, and any person disobeying the regulations in this respect will be liable to forfeit the amount of a day's pay afloat for every such offence." Every time the men went out on practice they were obliged to wear these belts, but whenever they were called on active service, they invariably neglected to put them on. They considered them to be cumbersome and to limit their ability to act efficiently. They were all experienced boatmen who would not normally wear lifebelts, and they also feared that they would be trapped under a capsized boat if they wore them.

Captain Parry took the 100 metre tow line aboard and set off with the Lifeboat. Within the shelter of the Mersey, the sea state was moderate, but, as they cleared the Horse Channel, off East Hoyle Bank near Newcombe Knoll, the waves were being driven by the NW wind into the shallower water of the sandbanks with the ebbing tide giving a strong current against the wind. This action of the tidal current caused the waves to become steep and high: conditions were now very bad. The lifeboat was suddenly struck on the port bow by a big wave and capsized. The tow rope parted and all the men aboard were thrown into the sea. A lookout on the *Blazer* shouted to alert

The Liverpool lifeboat capsizing under tow from the tug Blazer

Captain Parry what had happened. He kept the upturned lifeboat in view as he gave orders to get back as quickly as possible to pick up the lifeboatmen adrift in the water. Since they had thick clothing and heavy oil-skins, their only hope of keeping alive was to grab some floating object, such as an oar. Captain Parry ordered his men to throw lines to the survivors so that they could be pulled close enough to be helped aboard. The Master of the lifeboat was sighted in the water and the tug was manoeuvred so that he drifted past the paddle wheel of the *Blazer* and could be dragged aboard, by which time he was unconscious, although he recovered. Four of the men struggling in the waves were rescued by the crew of the *Blazer*, unfortunately seven were lost. Two men had managed to get hold of the lines thrown from the tug, but were unable to hold on in the icy seas and steep waves. Some of the rescued men had been struck by parts of the lifeboat as they were thrown into the sea, Henry Collins had an injured leg. Although a man could not survive long in the icy waters in January, had they been wearing their lifebelts, more would certainly have been saved, since the tug returned to pick them up as quickly as possible.

When all hope for survivors had been abandoned, Captain Parry continued to the Northwest Lightship, but it was still too rough to come alongside and take off the survivors of the wreck of the *Lelia*. The *Blazer* then returned to Liverpool with a melancholy tale to tell - of further loss of life and no rescue of the shipwrecked men. She was met on the way back by the steam tug *Royal Arch* which had been chartered by the Miller family (sons Henry and Edwin and son-in-law Capt. James Duguid) as soon as they heard news of the loss of the *Lelia* which had their brother Thomas Miller aboard. They hailed the *Blazer* - but Captain Parry was unable to give them any news about the fate of their brother.

The upturned lifeboat was subsequently washed ashore at Bootle. It took 100 men to turn her over on the beach. She had sustained some damage, her air-tight compartments on each side were stoved in. Ten lifebelts were found still stowed aboard.

The 7 lifeboatmen who lost their lives in the capsize of Liverpool No 1 lifeboat were all married and 11 young children were now without fathers. The wife of one of the volunteers, George Hampson, had been seriously ill and the news of her husband's death was too much for her - she died that evening. A request was made for donations to assist the families of those lost - the MDHB gave their usual contribution of £500, while the Royal Humane Society gave £100. A writer to the Liverpool newspapers urged more people to contribute to raise a similar sum (several thousands of pounds) to that raised for the loss of Point of Ayr lifeboat in 1857. The writer explained that though some people might be reluctant to contribute because the men were not wearing lifebelts, yet they were a courageous body of men, ever ready at all hours of the day and night to risk their own lives to save the lives of others.

A contemporary illustration shows the capsize of the Liverpool No 1 lifeboat. The engineer, Thomas Gallon, of the tug *Blazer* was awarded a silver medal by the Liverpool Shipwreck and Humane Society for the skill displayed in saving the master of the lifeboat and members of the crew. The lifeboatmen saved were Thomas Hudson (master), Griffith Thomas, John Amell and Henry Collins. Those lost were Robert Clarke, Bernard Murphy, Henry Green, George Hampson, Peter Martindale, James Martindale and James Bannin.

Chapter 9

The consequences

The Miller family was in the distressing situation of knowing that the *Lelia* had sunk and news had reached them that wreckage including three of her four ship's boats had been driven ashore off Formby. They also knew that there were some survivors on the North West Lightship. After the attempt by the Liverpool Lifeboat to reach the survivors had failed so disastrously on Sunday, they still did not know who from the *Lelia* had survived and with what injuries.

The next morning, Monday 16th January, the winds had abated somewhat and the Miller brothers (Henry and Edwin Miller and their brothers-in-law Capt. James Duguid and timber merchant Mr. Keverigan) set out again in the steam tug *Royal Arch* under the command of Capt. Davis to pick up the survivors of the loss of the *Lelia* who were still aboard the N.W. Lightship, hoping that the survivors would include Thomas. The sea state was less rough than the day before and, on the way out, they met the steam tug *Slasher* of the Old Tug Company which had already taken off the survivors from the NW Lightship and was bringing them to Liverpool. The survivors were hailed and questioned about the whereabouts of Thomas Miller and one pointed his hand to the seabed. This news confirmed the worst fears of the Miller family. The 12 survivors were then transferred to the *Royal Arch*, where they were offered warm drinks, food and clothes and taken to Liverpool. The survivors praised the conduct of Thomas Miller and one even said he would have sacrificed his own life to have spared Thomas Miller or Capt. Skinner.

Of the 8 passengers, 2 pilots and 49 crew who set out on the *Lelia*, only 12 survived, 47 being lost. None of the passengers, pilots or officers survived. As well as the collection for the families of the lifeboatmen lost, a collection was arranged, with Mr. Charles Campbell acting as treasurer, for the families of those lost aboard the *Lelia*. He contributed £20 and other major contributors were Crenshaws (ship managers, £50), Fawcett, Preston & Co. (engine builders, £40) and H. E. Moss (official owner, £20).

At the Board of Trade inquiry held on 26-28 January at Liverpool, the evidence available was presented. A verbatim account is included as an appendix. One of the main questions was "Why did she sink?" As is usual in a major disaster, several factors contributed.

- The carpenter was drunk when the small stores were delivered by the builders, so that blocks to the hawse pipes, sluice keys and rowlocks for the boats were not readily available when needed.
- The anchors were only partially brought inboard, leaving their flukes on the bulwark rail. This allowed water in through the anchor hatches which could not be closed. Some reports mention that the crown of an anchor may have damaged the foredeck.
- Steel ships were new technology and there had been cases of rivets popping and plates leaking when a ship was driven hard into rough seas.
- Blockade runners were designed to lie low in the water to avoid detection. They were therefore susceptible to being swamped by big waves.

- There were a lot of very experienced men aboard. Over confidence may have meant that the serious nature of their plight was realised too late.
- When the boats arrived at the Lightship, there was no rapid way to get on board, so men were overcome by the cold while holding on to lines thrown to them.
- Finally and most importantly, the weather was truly dreadful. The wind, waves and cold all contributed to the huge loss of life.

If *Lelia* had arrived safely in Bermuda, she would have been too late to render any assistance to the Confederate cause as a blockade runner. The assault on Fort Fisher, guardian of the passage into Wilmington was repulsed by the garrison under Colonel Lamb on Christmas Eve 1864 . The Union forces regrouped and their attack on 15 January 1865 was successful. Wilmington was now closed to blockade runners. Charleston was still open in principle, although the blockading force was strong. The last blockade runner to get into Charleston was *Chicora* (built by Millers as *Let her B*) on 16 February 1865. The only ports available after mid February were on the gulf coast and they were accessible to shallow draft vessels only. The Liverpool-built *Colonel Lamb* was transferred from running into Wilmington when Fort Fisher fell, and taken to run into Galveston in Texas, but was found to have too deep a draft, so returned to Liverpool without breaking the blockade. She was later sold to Greek interests, re-named *Bouboulina*, and sank on 29 November 1867 with the loss of 12 lives after a boiler explosion while at anchor above New Ferry in the Mersey. Her wreck is still marked on the modern seachart, but I doubt if there is anything left to see on the seabed.

Since blockade runners were no longer needed, the ships being built at Liverpool were now worth much less. The heavy commitment to building blockade runners at Liverpool was beginning to produce impressive results: for instance, Jones Quiggin launched four

*The sinking in the Mersey in 1867 after an explosion
aboard the Greek war-steamer Bouboulina
which had been launched as the blockade runner
Colonel Lamb*

identical blockade runners at the same time on 25 February 1865. The two sister ships to *Lelia* being built by Millers, the *Ray* and *Abigail*, were registered on 17 March 1865 as owned by William Cowley Miller. They were then sold off cheaply.

The loss of Thomas Miller was a disaster for the Miller family business. Thomas had been groomed to take over the business. The health of his father, William Cowley Miller, deteriorated and he died in 1869, aged 64. Although he had owned the freehold to an extensive shipyard and a graving dock, the business closed the next year. Thomas Miller left a wife and two children, one of whom, also named Thomas, worked for Fawcett & Preston, before becoming a lecturer at the Liverpool Mechanics Institute.

*Launch of five ships from the yard of Jones Quiggin
in February 1865. The four blockade runners were
named Widgeon, Snipe, Curlew and Plover
and the fifth ship was a screw steamer for an
Egyptian company.*

The boom of shipbuilding on the Mersey was over, but Liverpool as a port continued to expand. The priority use of land was for further docks and within a few decades shipbuilding at Liverpool had ceased. The Birkenhead side of the Mersey continued to build ships with Lairds (later Cammel Lairds) active until the 1990s.

On 31st May 1865, James Wilson, skipper of the Fleetwood fishing vessel *Elizabeth & Emma* found a body of a well dressed person in his nets some 10 miles out to sea. A reward had been offered for the recovery of the body of Thomas Miller, but after inspection it was realised that it was Commander Arthur Sinclair's body. His skeletal remains were still clothed, even to his cravat held in place by the gold and agate pin. His overcoat was still buttoned up and he had retained his watch in his breast pocket. The pocket watch had stopped at 4.10 - approximately the time the *Lelia* was abandoned.

This watch led to the definite identification of the body by Liverpool police since it had been bought in Liverpool.

The contemporary newspaper report describes the style of cravat worn by Arthur Sinclair as Dundreary, after the fictional comic character, Lord Dundreary, a brainless and be-wiskered English aristocrat who appeared in the successful play 'Our American Cousin' by Tom Taylor. This led to the creation of clothing in the style worn by Dundreary: a puffed-up cravat for example. Ironically, this was the play, then popular in America too, that President Abraham Lincoln attended on 14 April 1865 when he was assassinated.

An inquest was called at Fleetwood on 2nd June 1865 at the Steamer Hotel. In attendance was Richard Taylor, formerly Paymaster of the CSS *Florida*. Taylor was living in Liverpool at the time, following his release in February 1865 by Union authorities after the *Florida* was illegally captured in the port of Bahia. He informed the committee that he identified the body for the police from the watch, clothing and accompanying documents that related to a £1,300 deposit with Crenshaw and Company of Liverpool. Taylor told the local newspaper that Sinclair had left instructions, in the event of death or capture, that £100 be paid from this sum to each of his sons, the remainder to his wife Lelia and his younger children. According to Taylor, Sinclair had run the blockade successfully from Bermuda to Wilmington on several occasions and this deposit was presumably profits from his exploits. Taylor added that Federal forces had since occupied Norfolk, Virginia and had 'ejected Mrs Sinclair and her family from their home with great barbarity.'

The funeral of Arthur Sinclair who died aged 55, took place on 3rd June 1865 in Fleetwood and was attended by two of his sons, Arthur(jr) and Terry(jr). His gravestone bears the inscription 'Sacred to the memory of Captain Arthur Sinclair of Norfolk Virginia who perished in the wreck of the *Lelia* - January 14th 1865. Not lost but gone before.' Arthur Sinclair's eldest son Arthur(jr), who lived to be 88, had served on the CSS *Alabama* right up to her final battle with the USS *Kearsage*. He wrote a book of his experiences aboard. He had married in 1857 and had two children named Arthur and Lelia Imogene. The name Lelia lived on! Arthur Sinclair's third son, George Terry(jr), had served on the CSS *Florida* and also wrote a memoir of his experiences.

The submarine warfare expert Hunter Davidson had been sent to England to acquire materials for mines and torpedos. This material was put aboard the newly built blockade runner *Run Her* and when she left under a British flag and captain, Davidson was aboard. On reaching Terceira in the Azores, her captain ran her into Angra Bay but she grounded. The ship was stuck firmly and later broke up in storms. This was another blockade runner lost on her maiden voyage. Hunter Davidson returned to Britain and set out again with more specialist supplies in the *City of Richmond* but was diverted to assist in equipping the CSS *Stonewall* which had been built in France. When in Funchal, Madeira, in February 1865 Commander Hunter Davidson learned of the fate of his colleague, he said "What an awful thing the loss of the *Lelia*. To death in battle we become reconciled, for it is not unexpected and leaves its reward; but such a death as poor Sinclair, after 42 years' service...."

The American Civil War ended in June 1865. Some Europeans had expected the US government to honour loans made to the Confederate Government, but this was not to be the case. Many who had made big profits on paper ended up with nothing. There was a glut of potential blockade runners and many of these vessels were sold to South American interests for a fraction of their cost.

Some of the Confederate Navy personnel did not wish to risk returning to America where they might be prosecuted. James Bulloch remained in Liverpool. Commander John Maffitt, of the CSS *Florida*, came to Liverpool and took the Board of Trade examination so that he could act as master of a British-flagged merchant vessel.

After the end of the civil war the US government demanded recompense from Britain for the damage caused to their merchant marine by the Confederate warships such as the *Florida* and *Alabama* that had been built in Britain. Since the largest claim was from the actions of the *Alabama*, this came to be known as the 'Alabama Claim'. The initial claim was disputed, but in 1873 after International Arbitration (with representatives from USA, UK, Italy, Brazil and Switzerland meeting in Geneva) this was reduced to $15.5 million. This was the first time that an International Arbitration had been agreed and was the prototype for the League of Nations and then the UN.

Chapter 10
The discovery

It had long been known that two historic vessels built on the Mersey, the *Resurgam* and *Lelia*, had been lost in Liverpool bay. At various times in the past, the wrecks now known to be the *Calcium* and the *Letty* were thought to be candidates for the wreck of the *Lelia*. But as their identities became established, it was necessary to look elsewhere. After the discovery of the pioneering submarine *Resurgam* in 1995 which was only 30 tons, it was promising to conduct a thorough search for the much larger *Lelia*. She was a 600 ton steel ship and should give a sizeable magnetometer signal even if she was mostly under the seabed.

Information from the time of the loss of the *Lelia* indicated that she sank about 1.5 miles W by S of the Northwest Lightship. Indeed her masts were reported as still sticking out of the water. The MDHB would then have removed this obstruction to shipping. At that date, divers were able to get to the seabed to help in salvaging vessels but there was no record of such a salvage. More probably, the MDHB would have lowered large explosive charges to the base of each mast, to topple them. Then they would have checked that there was sufficient clearance, exploding more charges if needed. Their wreck records do not include any information about these activities.

To find the wreck, it was necessary to locate the position of the Northwest Lightship in 1865. The Northwest Lightship had been moved several times. It was initially at the entrance to the Rock (or Horse) Channel, then somewhat further out to sea and finally about 6 miles west of the Bar Lightship until it was removed altogether in the 1970s. From sea charts of 1865, I located the position of the Northwest Lightship at that date and then identified the most appropriate search area. There were about 50 Kingfisher fasteners (reports from trawlers of where their gear had snagged) in the area and I searched each in turn from the surface using a magnetometer and echo sounder. The magnetometer measures the intensity of the earth's magnetic field at the surface of the sea. Since this is sufficiently modified by large iron objects underwater, it is an easy way to find relatively shallow iron wrecks. The fifteenth site I explored in 1996 gave a magnetometer signal of a change in the surface magnetic field intensity of 2%, corresponding to around 1,000 tons of iron at that depth. At low water the depth of water is 20 metres to the seabed, and the echo sounder showed wreckage rising 6m off the seabed.

Diving in Liverpool Bay is not straightforward. There are strong tidal currents which a diver cannot swim against and which stir up the silt and sand making underwater visibility poor. The best time to dive is at neap tides which have the least currents and which occur for a few days every fortnight. Then, at low water slack, which conveniently occurs about midday at Liverpool, there will be no current and the best visibility. As well as current, wind is a factor. There is a long fetch (i.e. no protection from the nearby coast) from directions west through to north (as the *Lelia* found when in a NW storm) so the wind should be moderate (force 4 or less). The wreck site is only about 8 nautical miles from Hilbre Island and 12 miles from New Brighton. Ironically, in diving this site, I set off in my boat from Liverpool Marina which is based in Brunswick Dock, close to where the *Lelia* was built by Millers. Their shipyard has long since closed, but the Marina boat yard is busy with boats being repaired, a reminder of the active shipbuilding of previous times.

As soon as the weather allowed, I led a team to dive this site, but with poor underwater visibility, I found rectangular vertical objects which didn't look very ship-like. Perhaps this was an abandoned container of modern origin. Returning in better visibility, one paddle wheel was clearly visible and I recognised that the rectangular objects were the boilers which, being early low pressure boilers, were not the later cylindrical shape. This was almost certainly the *Lelia*. The position of the wreck is at latitude 53° 29.26' North, longitude 3° 23.04' West (with wgs84 datum). At low water (neap tide) the sandy seabed is 19 metres below surface.

On a subsequent dive, I found a lobster which I put in my goody bag and tied to the shot line. Exploring some more, I found a line of plumose anemones in the sand. They attach themselves to solid objects and this looked like the rim of a bowl. Digging away the sand from around it, I could feel the shape of it - it was not a bowl, but a bell. I was able to get it out of the sand easily and then expose its surface. I read 'LELIA 1864'. Now I had definite evidence that this was the wreck that had been sought for so long. To raise the 9 Kg bell, I needed my goody bag, so I extended my good fortune to the lobster and returned it to roam freely on the wreck.

I have dived the wreck regularly since as 'salvor in possession' and am pleased that divers have respected the wreck and left it much as it was when I found it and reported it to the Receiver of Wreck. Because of the way in which *Lelia* was abandoned with all the crew and passengers on her deck aft, I did not expect to find any human remains in the wreck. In 1997 the wreck was visited by the Archaeological Dive Unit who advised that it was not appropriate to designate it as an historic wreck at that time.

The bronze bell from Lelia

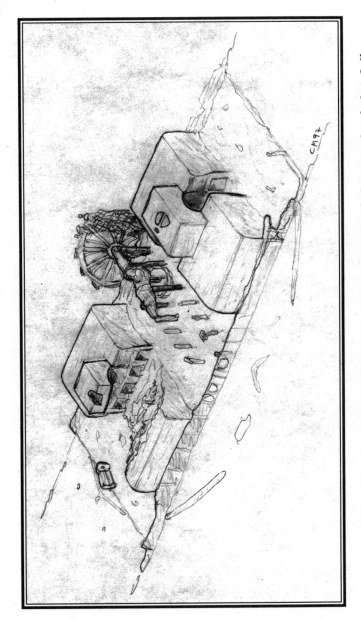

A sketch of the current appearance on the seabed of the wreck of the Lelia

The wreck lies with bows pointing NW and stern SE. The only area that rises substantially from the seabed is admidships and is the engine area. She had four low pressure boilers of square cross section with two forward of the paddles and two astern. The stern boilers are in good condition and the smoke collector lies above and between them. One can swim through the tunnel between these boilers. The forward port boiler is heavily damaged though the starboard one is fairly complete and has part of the smoke collector above it. The cylinder of the starboard engine is visible with the overhead shaft and paddle wheel in place. The paddle wheel has netting draped over it. There is no sign of the port paddle wheel. Just forward of the boilers lies a winch. The bow and stern are almost completely covered in sand and one clue as to which is the bow is some anchor chain. There is a lot of broken crockery and glass on the seabed - some of which I have dated as contemporary with the sinking.

Quite a lot is known of the design and construction of the *Lelia*. Her registration gives basic details and the report to the Board of Trade Enquiry (see Appendix) gives further details as provided by Edwin Miller of Millers shipbuilders and Herman Sillem of Fawcett's, the engine builders. The engines of her sister ship *Abigail* are illustrated in a contemporary book (by Burgh) and, though they are described as designed by James Watt of Birmingham, they will be similar to those installed by Fawcett's. The engines were of a very simple design: the port and starboard engine each had one cylinder with a single piston that drove a shaft overhead which was directly connected to the paddle wheel on that side. The cylinders rocked about a transverse axis, so that the piston could drive the shaft directly, hence they were known as oscillating engines. The paddle wheels had a feathering mechanism which allowed the angle of the floats to be varied as the wheel rotated so giving higher efficiency.

Plans of a somewhat larger steel blockade runner *Hope* exist in a contemporary book (edited by Rankine) and models of the *Hope* are

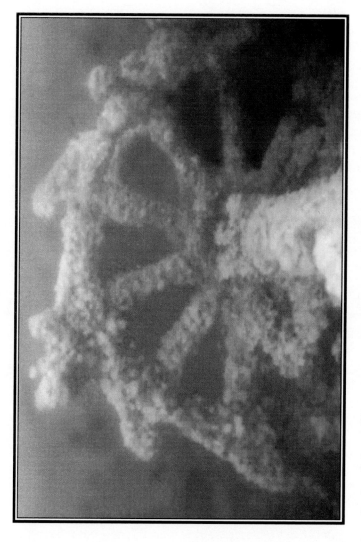

The starboard paddle wheel of Lelia underwater, covered with plumose anemones.

in the Maritime Museum on Merseyside and in the Mariners Museum, Newport News, Virginia. A plan of the rigging and hull of the *Lelia* exists and is illustrated. Some further details come from the newspaper report of her trials and from the reports of Union spies and are reproduced as appendices. Based on this information, I have constructed a picture of how she would have looked.

It is also of interest to establish what cargo she was carrying. Again the Board of Trade Enquiry and Union spy reports are available. These agree that coal was her main cargo: in the fore and aft hold as well as 340 tons in the bunkers. The coal in the holds (about 120 tons) was placed amidships to make room for the cargo in the wings. This cargo in the wings was placed up to the bulkheads, fore and aft and consisted of 40 tons of iron in the fore hold and the remainder (45 tons) was in the after hold. This was described as general cargo, mainly hardware and machinery. One Union spy describes the cargo being loaded as 'steel in bars, lead, boiler plates, army spades, casks supposed to contain shot, etc'. A later Union spy reported the loading of a 2 cwt case directed to Mr McLeish Bermuda, 20 casks of iron, baskets of potatoes, onions and other vegetables.

Because of the currents and waves, the hull of the *Lelia* has been corroded down to the level of the seabed except for the engines and boilers. This makes it difficult to explore the cargo she was carrying. In 2003 an attempt was made to investigate the stern hold as part of the Wreck Detectives TV programme, but poor weather meant little was achieved.

Visibility on the wreck can be as good as 5 to 8 metres in summer. There are often shoals of smallish fish sheltering near the wreck. The currents can be strange, especially in settled weather: up until low water Liverpool the surface current is strong and directed out (NW) from Liverpool and the Dee, while at the seabed the current turns earlier and at low water is already inward (SE). Neap tides are essential to avoid currents of over 1 knot.

The serious damage to the port side of the *Lelia* could have several causes. The wreck site is where large ships anchor waiting for the tide to enter Liverpool and a ship's anchor could have smashed through part of the wreck. Another possibility is that during the last war, the wreck was mistaken for an enemy submarine and depth charged. The amount of sand covering the wreck is presumably just that which has built up over the last century.

It turns out that some local fishermen knew of the wreck but did not have any idea of its true identity. It is indeed surprising that a wreck rising 6 metres off the seabed in the approaches to Liverpool was not charted during more than 130 years.

As a coincidence, another Miller-built blockade runner was lost with Arthur Sinclair aboard. This was the *Mary Celestia* which sank on the coast of Bermuda where she now lies on a sandy bottom in 16 metres with her starboard paddle wheel standing prominently from the seabed, just like the *Lelia*.

The wreck of the *Lelia* in Liverpool Bay serves as a monument to an exciting time, when Liverpool shipbuilding and the American Civil War were closely interwoven. *Lelia* never fulfilled her destiny but her wreckage still reminds us of the history of those times.

Lelia

Another wreck of a blockade runner

There is another wreck of a blockade runner off the coast of Britain that has been explored by divers. This is the *Iona(II)*.

She was built in 1863 by James & George Thomson at Govan on the Clyde, designed as a fast Clyde River excursion steamer, an iron paddle steamer of 250 ft length, 25 ft beam and 9 ft draft. She had a twin cylinder oscillating engine (as had the *Lelia*). Since Clyde excursion steamers were proving very capable at blockade running, they were much sought after. The *Iona(II)* was bought second hand in late November 1863 for £20,000 ($100,000) which was more than she had cost when new.

She had been purchased by Charles Hopkins Bostier of Richmond, Virginia and he arranged for her to set off to Nassau with a valuable cargo. After leaving Cobh in Ireland (then called Queenstown), she proceeded to a very secluded anchorage to the east of Lundy Island. This may have been to meet another ship bringing war supplies or may have been to make repairs after storm damage. At this anchorage, she was run down in fog and sank on 2 February 1864, although 39 of her crew, including Captain Chapman, were saved.

Her cargo must have been valuable since attempts were made to salvage her. The wreck position was buoyed and a steam tug from the Liverpool Steam Tug Company arrived on the site on 19 May 1864. A diver was sent down at low water to place a buoy at each end of the wreck, but he got entangled in the wreckage and only got free with difficulty, surfacing unconscious. He had recovered by the next day and inspected the wreck, reporting that it was broken across the aft section, and there was nothing to salvage. A later report describes the funnel and a few fathoms of chain being recovered and stating that the wreckage was then freely available to any diver.

This wreck was subsequently rediscovered in 1976. I dived it in 1987 when the four large low-pressure boilers were very conspicuous, lying north to south. The engines could be seen between them. The wreck is in 22 metres. It lies out of the area of very strong currents which can sweep around Lundy, and the current is quite weak on the flood tide, so the site can be a bit silty at times. There was a very large conger eel population on the wreck at that time. It is close to a much more modern wreck, the MV *Robert* which sank in 1975. Indeed it was divers exploring the *Robert* who rediscovered the *Iona(II)* since the two wrecks are only 50 metres apart with the *Iona(II)* lying to the southwest of the *Robert*. In 1989 *Iona(II)* was designated an historic wreck, with permission needed to dive on it. The restricted area which contains the wreck is centred at 51° 11.056' North, 4° 38.854' West, in the wgs84 datum.

*A*ppendix

*T*he crew and passengers of the *L*elia

The birthplace, if not given, is Liverpool. The street addresses given may well have been lodging houses for those sailors not from Liverpool.

Name	Position	Age			Origin
Thomas Buxton Skinner	Master	38	m d		b Henrico, Virginia
Lauritz Jonas Peterson	First Mate	31	d		Daulby St, b Copenhagen
George De Lacy	Second Mate	26	d		Parliament St, b Savannah
James Baxter Harrison	Third Mate	24	d		Greenfield St, Old Swan
John McKinnon	Carpenter	31	d		Greenland St, b Glasgow
William Smith	Boatswain	24	m		Spring St, b Shetland
Henry Morris	Able Seaman	33	d		Clarence Grove
Michael Curry	Able Seaman	28	d		Waterloo Road
Andrew Brodie	Able Seaman	32	m		Earle St, b Dumbarton
James McCallum	Able Seaman	28	d		Greenland St, b Prince Edward I.
William Everetts	Able Seaman	21	d		Simpson St
James Kewin	Able Seaman	22	d		Cemaes St, b Virginia
Edward Smith	Able Seaman	28	d		Milford St, b Dublin
Henry Scott	Able Seaman	25	m		Milford St
Tynan Danford Oby	Seaman	25	s		Jordan St, b Canada
John Lindstrom	Seaman	24	s		Lander St, b Stockholm
John Hughes	Watchman	32	d		Epsom St
Thomas Grammall	Boy	16	d		Duke St, b Girvan
Thomas Herriott	Boy	19	d		Roscommon St, b Hampshire
John Clarke	Steward	40	d		Bury St, b Westmoreland

James Tinker	Steward	28	m	Derby Road, b Manchester
William Taylor	Steward	18	d	Roscommon St
Patrick Kennedy	Cook	34	d	Paget St, b Newry
Daniel McLoughlin	Cook	27	d	Stone St
John Miller	Cook	40	d	Redcross St, b London
James France	1st Engineer	32	d	Walmsley St, b Lanark
James McClym	2nd Engineer		d	Flinders St, b Port Patrick
Charles Francis Middleton	Engineer	33	d	Islington Pl, b S Carolina
John Frederick Lyons	Engineer	21	d	Canning Place, b Southampton
John Kempton	Fireman	29	d	Slade St, b Stranraer
William Kelly	Fireman	24	d	Westmoreland St, b Belfast
Hugh Magee	Fireman	22	s	Ascot St, b County Down
Timothy O'Brien	Fireman	30	m	Burlington St, b Cork
Thomas Wilson	Fireman	34	d	Saltney St
Robert Kenney	Fireman	25	s	Athol St
Samuel Cormick	Fireman	27	s	Raymond St, b Ballymena
John Casey	Fireman	27	d	Regent St, b Dublin
Thomas Kinsel	Fireman	36	d	Barlow St, b Wexford
George Murray	Fireman	26	d	Blake St, b Belfast
John Burke	Fireman	43	d	Tatlock St, b Tipperary
Peter Devlin	Fireman	27	m	Darwin St, b Glasgow
Bartholomew Shaw	Fireman	24	d	Bentinck St, b Sheffield
John Jackson	Fireman	25	s	Newport St, b Manchester
Thomas Sheddon	Fireman	23	d	Blackstone St, b Renfrew
John Cunningham	Fireman	38	d	Russell St, b Edinburgh
John Kelly	Fireman	40	d	New Hedley St, b Derry
William Halpin	Fireman	22	d	Slade St, b Kilkenny
Peter Laverty	Fireman	36	d	Dryden St, b Glasgow
Joseph Keating	Boy	17	d	Cranmer St
William Williams	Pilot	46	m d	Chatsworth St
Magnus Park	Pilot		d	Cork, Ireland
Arthur Sinclair	CSN Cmdr	54	m d	62 Canning St, b Norfolk, Virginia
Thomas C. Cuddy	CSN Gunner		d	b Charleston, GA
Thomas Miller	shipbuilder	28	m d	Liverpool
C. L. Hobson	agent		d	

John B. Cropper	agent		m	d	Willows Breck Road
James William Clarke	clerk	25	s	d	
Mr. Campbell	passenger			d	
Mr. Gerchart	passenger			d	

Where known m indicates married and s single.
Those who perished on the wreck are indicated by d.

Registration of Lelia

Lelia was registered at Liverpool as a British vessel on 10th January 1865.

She was described as a steel paddle steamer owned by Henry Elias Moss of Rumford Place, Liverpool. She had a steel framework with clinker construction (i.e. overlapping steel plates). The only closed-in space above her main deck was described as a bunk for crew accommodation, under the topgallant forecastle (also known as a hurricane deck). She was schooner rigged with two masts with an elliptical shaped stern. Her port number was 11, and her official number 51,407. She had one deck. Her gross tonnage was 640, and her register tonnage was 432. She had two engines of the combined power of 300 h.p. Her length was 252.1 feet, her breadth 30 feet, and her depth of hold 12.6 feet. The engines occupied 56.8 ft amidships. Her designated master was Thomas Buxton Skinner, certificate of competency no. 31276.

Note that register tonnage was calculated as volume: 1 ton being 100 cubic feet (2.83 m³). The gross tonnage was the volume below deck, the net tonnage allowed for deductions for the engines and crew accommodation. The expression tons burthen (or burden) refers to carrying capacity which was quoted as 1100 tons for *Lelia*.

Lelia

The entry in the Liverpool Shipping register for Lelia

-112-

Union spy reports

The following are transcripts of the reports by Union spies to the Union Consul in Liverpool, which were duly passed on to Washington. The report of the appearance of the *Lelia* followed a set convention, going from stern to bow. The grammar, spelling and punctuation are as in the originals.

11 January 1864:

I have the honor to enclose a description of the new paddle steamer "Lelia," built by W.C. Miller, which is now taking on board steel in bars, lead, boiler plates, Army spades, casks supposed to contain shot, etc. She is said to be going to Bermuda, but has not yet entered. She will likely sail this week. Report enclosed.

Report:

"Lelia" Steel plated, Two funnel, paddle steamer, Built by W.C. Miller at Liverpool in 1864. Rigged as a fore and aft Schooner of Liverpool, 430 tons register, 1110 tons burthen.

Length 265 feet, Breadth of beam 30 feet, Depth of Hold 15 feet, Marked draught of water 9 feet, fore and aft, Engine 300 horse power.

Hull slate color, plain stem, Round stern with four deadlights, name & port, in yellow letters on same, 6 dead lights, in port and starboard sides aft. 2 boats in iron swing davits, upon each side, abaft paddleboxes.

Poop, Iron railed round, Wheel, binnacle, Skylights, a Companion upon each side, on the forepart of same with the entrance to cabin on the lower deck.

Lower deck, mainmast, Patent Winch, Main hatch, Coal bunkers, after funnel, Steampipe forepart, Iron boxed round on deck, Bridge between paddle boxes, Iron railed, at lookout house, on the top of same containing a Wheel and Binnacle, House with rooms underneath, Fore funnel, steam pipe forepart, Iron boxed round on deck, Coal Bunkers, fore hatch, Patent winch, Foremast.

Stormtopgallant forecastle, Iron railed, Forecastle hatch, Iron railed, Capstan, Iron Swing Davit for fish tackle, 2 iron stocked anchors.

Masts, Booms, Gaffs, Companions, & Skylights bright, Mastheads & Funnels black, Bulwarks etc. drab, Boats white."

January 14 1865:

The Lelia Paddle Wheel Blockade Runner has a poop deck astern level with the bulwarks which is nearly 4 ft high. There is a rail around it. Underneath is a very handsome cabin fitted out in great grandeur. Above the poop deck there is 2 small boats and 2 others between this cabin and the 2 funnels, these last 2 can be seen under from a distance. The 2 funnels are very broad but not high inclined very much toward the stern and are painted black. There is two masts. Steam winches fore and aft. Hurricane deck at the Front. The ship has a greyish color and altogether a very rakish and fine appearance. There is 4 portholes, paddle boxes - that is very high, small house, the bridge between paddle boxes about 1 ft higher at a short distance looks level with the paddle boxes. The boards for 2 ft in depth and the full breadth are taken out of the sides of the boxes. The paddles can be seen from the outside, very large floats and has 4 other patent floats on board in case of accident. It need not be wondered if at anytime she might not be turned into a piratical ship as she is in every particular made strong in preparation. In some places, the steel plates are no more than 1/4 inch in thickness. Below the deck it is 1/2 inch thick. The bulwarks are 1/2 inch steel plate riveted on angle iron every 3 ft apart. On every plate 4 ft apart there is a flat 1/4 inch plate 4 inches wide 30 inches long with 40 rivets to strengthen the ship generally. Engines 300 hp. She is most certainly going to Bermuda first, as I hear by Madeira. There is 2 passengers on board, Southern agents, besides Capt Sinclair who is to have charge of her when out there. A 2 cwt weighs case directed to Mr McLeish Bermuda. 20 casks of iron. Baskets of potatoes onions and other vegetables. I will hear soon if there is any talk of her going on any other move besides blockade running.

Board of Trade Enquiry

From the Liverpool Telegraph and Daily Shipping and Commercial Gazette of January 27, 28 and 30 covering the Enquiry held on 26, 27 and 28th. This is a verbatim report except some fractions are rendered in a more modern way. Also some differing or additional information contained in the briefer report in the Liverpool Mercury is added in braces. See notes at the end on some nautical terms.

Thursday 27 January 1865 in the new Appeal Court, Dale Street, Mr.T. B. Raffles, S.M., held an enquiry with Captains Harris and Baker, as nautical assessors, under the direction of the Board of Trade into the circumstances which attended the loss of the ill-fated steamer Lelia, which loss has cast such a deep gloom over this town, owing to there having perished with her no less than 47 persons, among whom were two gentlemen highly esteemed in town.
Mr. Hamel appeared to conduct the proceedings on behalf the Board of Trade, and Mr. Forshaw appeared for the owners of the ship.

Mr. Hamil made an opening statement to the following effect:- This is an enquiry into the loss of the steamship Lelia, which occurred on her outward passage from this port to Bermuda on 14th instant, when she was only some few miles beyond the N.W. Lightship on that day. She was an iron paddle steamer, built by Messrs. Miller and

Sons of Liverpool, and was owned by Henry Elias Moss of Rumford place, Liverpool. Her port number was 11, and her official number 51,407. She was schooner-rigged, clipper-built, had a steel framework, and one deck. Her gross tonnage was 640, and her register tonnage was 431. She had two engines of the combined horse power of 300 horses. Her length was 252 feet, her breadth 80 feet, and her depth of hold 12 feet. I propose to offer but a very short account of the matter, as all the officers belonging have unfortunately been lost with her. It appeared that she left Liverpool on the morning of the 14th January, in charge of Captain Thos. Buckston [Buxton] Skinner, her master, who held a certificate of competency, and her crew consisted of 49 [50] hands, all told. She had also on board two pilots, one from Liverpool and the other from Cork, and eight gentlemen, six of whom were going out to Bermuda, and two were going to leave her at Holyhead, and return to Liverpool in the steamtug that was to bring the pilot back, those two being Mr. Thomas Miller and Mr. James [H] Clarke[Clark]. The name of the Liverpool pilot was Williams. She would appear to been laden, having on board 85 tons [deadweight] of cargo and 460 tons of coals for ship's use. She proceeded to sea with the barometer in a very low state, and still falling. She was drawing at that time about 10.5 ft of water, and there was a strong gale blowing from the N.W. When she passed the Crosby Lightship the sea was beginning to break over her, and after passing the N.W. Lightship, she shipped a good deal of water, the fore deck being constantly filled with the heavy seas that broke over her. After a while it was noticed that the vessel appeared to be settling down by the head, and Captain Skinner thought it was desirable to put her [head] about and return to Liverpool. The vessel nearly lost her steerage way, but she got round by the assistance of a sail. After proceeding in the direction of Liverpool for some time the vessel got deeper in the water by the head, and the hatches burst open, the water getting into the hold, and the ship appeared to be in a sinking state. The engines were stopped, and the boats were ordered out to save life. Out of the four boats that were launched two only left in safety, the others being capsized and filled. Two of them reached the N.W. Lightship with 30 persons on board, when they were capsized, and all on board of them thrown into the water. Only twelve men got on board the lightship, and these were the boatswain and steward, the engineer's store-keeper, five firemen, and four sailors. There being altogether 59 persons on board, 47 [48] were drowned, amongst whom were the two pilots, 37 of the crew, the six gentlemen who were passengers, and the two who were going to Holyhead.

Mr. H. Murphy, out-door superintendent of the Sailor's Home, produced the ship's articles, from which it appeared that there were 49 of a crew, all told, on board of the ship.

Mr. John Hartnup, jun., assistant astronomer at the Liverpool Observatory, said:- At midnight on the 13th of January, the barometer read 28.55 [a low value], and fell from that time until 8:30 a.m. on the morning of the 14th, at which time it read 28.34. After that it rose rapidly, and it read at four o'clock in the afternoon 28.71. At eight o'clock at night it read 28.82. At eight o'clock in the morning the wind was SSE, and it was then a moderate breeze. Between eight and nine o'clock the wind changed from SSE to SSW, and it was blowing a slight breeze at nine a.m. It gradually increased in force from that time, the heavy portion of the wind blowing from west, as, between nine and eleven, had changed to that quarter, and at eleven it was blowing fresh. The gale continued through the whole of that day, and on to the morning of the 16th. It increased greatly from 9 o'clock on the morning of the 14th to 5 o'clock in the evening, when it was at its height. At a quarter past five there was a pressure of 21lbs to the square foot, which was what sailors called blowing strong. There was nothing extraordinary observable by the thermometer. There was no signal from Admiral Fitzroy hoisted that day, although there had been one hoisted on the 12th. At eleven o'clock on the 14th there was a pressure of 10lbs to the square foot. A pressure of 9lbs is a fresh breeze, and 15lbs is a strong one.

Edwin [Edward] Miller: I am a draughtsman to Messrs. Miller and Sons ship-builders of this town. I produce the profile of [and] the lower deck plan and mid-ship section of the steamer *Lelia*. [A sister ship in dock can be visited]. Her deep load line would be 10 feet 6 inches to which she might be safely loaded, and that would leave amidships a clear side of 2 feet 6 inches up to the covering board. Her bulwarks were 4 feet 6 inches in height, and were of steel. She had five wash ports on each side, level with the covering board, [these were hinged above deck level and opened outwards] and on each side she had four scuppers. She had a raised poop on her upper deck 4 feet 6 inches, level with the rail in the after part. She had no topgallant-forecastle, but she had a hurricane deck, with berths underneath from the foremast to within 12 feet of the stem which formed the house, the hurricane deck going over that portion to the stem, which was not used as a house. There were two openings in the sides of the hurricane deck for getting the anchor on board. There were no other deckhouses except the bridge on [top of] which the pilot-house was. She steered either from the bridge or from the wheelhouse aft. There was no other house aft. She had three lifeboats and one gig, each of them 23 feet long: each lifeboat had 7 feet beam [they had cork water-tight compartments]. They were double-banked lifeboats, pulling six oars. They were fitted with metal crutches or rollocks. There was fitted on the main deck a manhole 18 inches by 12 inches leading down to the forepeak. She had six bulkheads, and the forepeak would be 19 feet from the bulkhead to the stem [12 feet wide and 12 feet deep]. There was no other means of communication with the forepeak than the small manhole. Her forehold was 76 feet in length from the foremast bulkhead to the bulkhead before the bunker [with hatch 18 feet by 12 feet]. Her after hold was 42 feet[22 feet] in length between the bulkheads. The centre of gravity would be at 3 feet 5 inches before the paddle-shaft. The ship was plated with steel, and the frames were also of steel. The garboard streak was 3/8 th of an inch in thickness, and the bottom plates to the turn of the bilge 3/8 to 5/16. The sides and shear streaks 5/16th amidships. The shear streak was 3/8th,

5/16, and one quarter. The maindeck stringer plate was 3 feet 6 inches wide by a quarter in thickness amidships, tapering forward and aft to 2 feet, secured to the shear streak by the angles. In addition, there was a deck stringer fore and aft 12 inches wide by 1/4 in. thickness, excepting the weight of the engines and boilers. Diagonal stringers were introduced in the weight of the engines.

By Mr. Forshaw: I have given this information from the specification furnished to and excepted [accepted] by the owners, and the ship was completed by the builders. Other vessels of the same specification have gone across on a similar voyage.

By Mr. Hamel: There were two sluice valves to each bulkhead, working from the deck by means of a rod.

Mr. H. J. [Herman James] Sillem: I am an engineer, and partner with Messrs. Fawcett and Preston. We made the engines of the *Lelia*. They were oscillating engines, direct action, tubular boilers, the nominal horse power being 300. On the trial trip they worked up to 6.5 times their nominal power. The boilers were loaded at 30lbs pressure, and were proved to 60lbs by hydraulic pressure before being put on board. There were four boilers, two before and two abaft the engines, and were fired athwart ship. They were seated on kelsons specials [specially] provided as a bed for them. The bunkers were before and abaft the engines, and would contain about 340 tons of coal. [coal consumption was less than 50 tons a day at full power]. There was no other coal space.

Hugh Goold[Gould]:- I am a surveyor of Customs at Liverpool, and I have the clearance papers of the steamship *Lelia*, which consist of the manifest, contents and victualling bill, showing what she had on board, which was principally hardware [machinery and other things].

Andrew Brodie, able seaman: I joined the *Lelia* on the 10th, at the Carriers' Dock, which she left on Friday about eleven o'clock. We came to an anchor off Rock Ferry until the following day, when

between eight and nine a.m. we left the river. There was a strong
breeze, but the weather looked good. The wind was from NNW to
NW, and there was a fine good breeze. When we got the anchor up
we went ahead full speed. We took the starboard on board and left
the port anchor on the rail ready to be let go. I then went to the
wheel, and was there all day. I steered at the after wheel going down
the river. We got to the Bell Buoy about 12 o'clock. It was very cold,
and there was a good deal of water breaking over her. We were not,
however, shipping green seas, but when a sea struck her it would
break all over her. About one o'clock, after passing the Bell Buoy,
the sea was very much higher, and she shipped some heavy seas.
She did not pitch into it, but she shipped heavy. The effect was that
the guard rail athwart ships on the bridge was started by her
straining. I was then steering on the bridge. [There was sleet]. She
was slowed to get the port anchor on board, which was done. The
crown of both anchors then lay on deck, and the stock lay over the
rail. When the anchors were secured we went ahead full speed. After
that I observed that the forecastle or deckhouse [fore bulkhead] was
washed out, all our clothes were washed out. The covers on the
hurricane deck for the places where the anchors were taken in, were
not on and when the ship pitched into the seas, through these
openings, the space between the house and the stem filled and broke
in the bulkheads, and washed out the house. The bulkhead was made
of wood. The mens' berths and bedding and all were washed into the
waist, and went overboard through the washboards.
The court here adjourned until Friday.

Friday, the enquiry into the loss of the steamship *Lelia* was resumed,
before Mr. Raffles and Captains Baker and Harris, Mr. Hamel
appearing for the Board of Trade and Mr. Forshaw for the owners of
the vessel, as before.

Andrew Brodie, seaman, was again called, and continued his
evidence as follows:- Endeavours were made to pick up as much of
the men's bedding as possible, when it was washed out of the house.

The bedding was put over the grating of the stoke-hold [stoke-hole] to prevent the water going down. By this time the steamer began to settle down by the head, as the body of water that came on board was so great that it could not be got off as quickly as it came on. The decks were full of water to the raised bulkhead over the shaft of the engines. All the men were engaged at the time in picking up bedding and getting the pumps ready. The pumps were started soon after the bulkhead of the house was washed away. There was no water at the after pumps, which were worked by the donkey-engine. While they were at the pumps I went into the house to look for some of my clothes. I then saw down the scuttle water running in the forepeak in the form of an eddy, as if the water that had got in the forepeak was running away somewhere. [I noticed that one of the anchors was stowed slewed as if the peak of it had penetrated the deck, but did not check if it had]. I then went aft to the wheel, and told Captain Skinner that I thought the ship was sinking by the head. He then told the mate to go forward and see if anything was the matter, and when he came back to the bridge, he said to Capt. Skinner that he could not get far enough forward to see what was the matter for the water that was hanging forward as she was down by the head. The ship was shipping green seas at the time, and the whole of the after part of the house was washed away, and every sea washed something more away. It was dangerous to stand forward for being washed away, or something striking him. The pilot Williams came to the wheel-house and asked me whether we thought that there was anything the matter with the ship, and we, who were at the wheel, said we thought that she was settling. The pilot then called Captain Skinner, and the engines were slowed. The captain asked what was best to be done, and the pilot said he thought she would fetch Holyhead. The ship did not pitch into the sea so much when she was going slow. Captain Skinner said to the pilot that he thought it would be better to run back. While they were talking, she shipped a very heavy sea which shook here all over, and then the pilot told me to put the helm astarboard. She would not pay off with her helm hard astarboard, and he told me to put the wheel hard aport. We put the wheel hard aport and then the foretopmaststaysail was hoisted. She did not pay off very quickly, but went off 2.5 points. She lay there for a short time, and then orders were given to haul out the fore and aft foresail. She then payed off right before the wind, and was then put on full speed running back for Liverpool.

She went much easier than when head on to it, but with the weight of the water forward she shook all over. We were running the same way as the sea, and she still continued to ship seas. She would not steer by the wheel in the wheel-house, as she sometimes came up as much as two points and a half, owing, in a great measure to the seas striking her on the weather quarter, and the after wheel was connected. The men were frequently washed back and forward on the deck, so that they could not stand by the pumps. The pumps delivered the water on the deck, and increased that which was already on the deck. We were abreast of Great Ormshead when we put about to run back to Liverpool. She answered the after wheel very well for about an hour and a half, during which we were going about 7.5 knots, the tide being against them. When we were going along nicely a heavy sea struck her on the port quarter, and she came right up in the wind and would not answer her helm for some time. When she broached to, her head came up in the wind, and she lay in a trough of the sea for over fifteen minutes, and the foretopmaststaysail was blown away. The carpenter had been washed out of one of the wash boards, after a bed [it was confirmed that such a wash port was big enough for a man to be swept through]. When the vessel was first got before the wind the foresail was taken down, and when she broached to we hauled out the foresail and got her before the wind again. She went along steering badly for about an hour. She was so much down by the head that when a sea struck the rudder she threw Currie and I over the wheel. She was not going more than half speed at this time, but I could not tell what was done in the engine rooms. We got within three or four miles west of the N.W. Lightship, and then she would come up two or three points in the wind, until we were abreast of the lightship, and about four or five miles off it. She then came up in the wind [broached to] with her head to the northward, and became unmanageable. The engines were reversed, and she went full speed back to see if we would fetch her off the wind again, and the foresail was still standing, but she would not pay off. At this time she rolled very heavy and shipped a very heavy sea, when the fore hatches burst open. They burst open from below from the pressure of water and air in the compartment. The water on the deck was level with the combings of the hatch, and every time the ship rolled the water went down. The crew were then all aft, the covering board forward being level with the water.

The captain gave orders to lower the boats and the starboard waste[sic] boat on the lee was lowered first, with some hands in her. The two pilots got in first, and then followed some of the passengers and a great many of our own crew, so that there were from fourteen to sixteen people in that boat [in an orderly way]. I was standing at the wheel all this time, and I saw Captain Skinner go down into the boat and place the people in her. He then came on deck and gave orders for the port waist boat to be lowered. I never saw the starboard boat that was lowered first leave the ship. It was about 5o'clock when the boat was lowered, and was not dark. That boat must have sunk by being struck with the sponson. When the port lifeboat was lowered too many got into her, and the after davit was bent down to the water, and she half filled. The tackle was cut by one of the firemen who was in her, and she went away all clear. There were ten firemen, one seaman, and the second steward in that boat. [The second steward fell overboard and was pulled out by a fireman.] The port quarter boat was then lowered safely into the water with seventeen men in her. Captain Skinner then came to the wheel and said to Currie and I, "men, you not stand there any longer." We then left the wheel, and I went down the tackle and got into that boat on the port side. I said to Captain Skinner before I left the deck, "Captain Skinner, are you going in this boat" and he said "yes Brodie, go down and I'll follow you." There was no one then on board but the captain, Currie, and myself. As soon as I got into the boat the tackle was let go, and we pulled round the stem[stern] to the starboard side of the ship. When we got there I saw Captain Skinner and Currie hanging on by the after tackle, and the boat was down full of water. It was getting dark, and it looked as if the forward tackle was gone, and the boat was hanging on by the after tackle. We could not see what had become at the people in the boat, and we could not go near Captain Skinner and Currie to give them any assistance.

We went on towards the lightship, and when half way we saw three rockets go up from the ship, which we supposed were sent up by the captain and Currie. We got under the stem[stern] of the light-ship, and three lines were thrown to us. The first mate got hold of one of the lines and took a turn round the midship thwart, which brought the boat broadside on [under the stern]. A sea then struck the boat and capsized her, turning her keel up, and all the eighteen men were thrown into the water. Mr. Miller had been pulling an oar all the time, and he and I were under the lee side of the boat, and we got out and struck for the lightship. I got hold of one of the lines and got some distance up by it when the mate caught me by the leg and pulled me back into the water. I still held on by the rope, and Mr. Miller took hold of the same line with me, he having let go the smaller line which he at first caught. I had a turn round my hand of the rope, but we were too heavy for them to haul us all three up, and they were obliged to slack down the rope. When the rope was slacked the mate let go my leg and I saw no more of him. Mr. Miller was still holding on by the rope with me and by my coat with the other hand. A circular life buoy was thrown over, and I got inside it. I got my arms over the buoy [since I had no power in my hands], and I then said "Miller, you can hold on by me now, for you cannot pull me out of the life buoy." The men on board the lightship attempted to reeve the line through the vang block, and they slacked the line up, and both Mr. Miller and I went under water, and when I came up he was gone, and I never saw him again. I was then hauled on board.

There were [plenty of oars but] no rollocks in the life boat when I got into her, and we had to break up the boat hook to make thoul pins. I cannot say whether there had been rollocks when the boat lowered, but I know that they were in some of the boats when they were secured on board of the steamer. I pulled one oar myself. The rudder of the boat was washed away soon after we left the steamer, and we had to steer with the oars, only pulling to suit the sea, which was with us, as well as the wind. There were three more besides myself saved out of this boat, whose names are Smith (boatswain), Scott, and Obey.

When we bore up for Liverpool a signal of distress was made hoisting ensign union down. A steamer outward bound bore down to us and followed us for some distance, and could not catch us, then, seeing that we did not slow, she went away her course. This was the *Sovereign*, of Bristol, a steamer with two masts, and a red streak in her funnel. When we saw her turning round the ship was slowed, and oilcloth coats were hung up in the rigging as additional signals of distress. I cannot say whether the captain and pilots thought that the *Sovereign* was running back to Liverpool, but I always thought myself that the master of the Sovereign thought we were making a fool of him. I believe that if that steamer had come up with us every one on board the *Lelia* would have been saved. She broached to directly after the steamer turned away from us, and when the engines were slowed. We had two small guns on board, but they were not used for signalling. We, the survivors, twelve in all, got on board of the lightship on Saturday night, and were taken off on Monday morning.

By Captain Harris: I saw coals both in the main and fore holds, but none on deck. The ship was drawing 10 feet 5 inches aft when we were filling the water on the Wednesday before leaving. We were running back for Liverpool at the time the carpenter was lost. I have not passed an examination as mate, but I mean to do it.

Mr. Raffles: Why don't you go in for it! You have given your evidence in a most intelligent manner.

By Captain Baker:- I thought the weather was very fine that morning when we went out, but when we got to the Bell Buoy, if I had been consulted, I certainly should have advised going back. [I have been sailing in American ships as an officer for 15 years].

James Tinker: I was second steward of the *Lelia*, there being five stewards on board. It was my duty to attend upon the officers and passengers in the cabin. We had six passengers on board. Messrs. Miller and Clarke were to leave at Holyhead. There were as passengers, Captain Arthur Sinclair, Mr. Culldy [Cuddy], Charles L. Hobson, James H. Croper [John B. Cropper], Mr. Gearchaet [Gerchart], and Mr. Campbell, who were going to Bermuda. I left the wreck in the small lifeboat from the port midship. I cannot say how many, but I think there were fifteen men in the boat when we left the ship. We had no rollocks in the boat, and we hoisted an oar over the bow, the blade of the oar acting as a sail. We steered with an oar. When we got to the light-ship three of the cooks jumped overboard to get hold of the line that was hanging over the side of the lightship, but they were all three drowned. I sat in the stem of the boat, and tried to keep her head on to the sea when the men were being pulled on board the lightship. Some were lost and some were saved. I got on board last, and the boat broke adrift after. Our boat was not capsized.

William Smith: I was boatswain of the *Lelia*. I joined her on the 12th January. I remember passing the N.W. Lightship and she was shipping water before then, but she shipped heavy seas after that. I believe we were as far down as the Formby Lightship when we got the port anchor on the rail. A good while after that I was sent forward to see where the water was coming in, and I put my foot in the scuttle and my foot went down. The water was swirling and gurgling in the manhole. It was coming in by the hawse pipes, through the anchor openings in the hurricane deck, and over all. While we were stowing the port anchor she was shipping water so heavily that the second mate was washed off the hurricane deck down on the main deck. We stuffed blankets and pillows into the chain pipes to keep out the water. I heard the pilot calling out to man the boats before the ship was put about to return back. The boats were lowered flush with the gunwale, and Captain Sinclair [Skinner] came and ordered them to be hoisted up again, as, he said, the ship was all right. They were hoisted up and secured. After we put about we hoisted our ensign union down, and the steamer Sovereign chased us for about a quarter of an hour, but we were going faster than her, and she put about again, and bore away on her own course. When we were covering up the gratings to prevent the water going down to put the fires out, the N.W. Lightship was reported off the lee bow. I soon after heard that they were clearing away the boats, and I got into a boat on the starboard waist, but there was such confusion that I got out again, and then went to the port boat, and began to look for thouls. I could find none, but I got into the boat and she was lowered safely. After we got thouls made of the boat hook, we got pushed off with a great deal of difficulty and kept before the wind by steering with our oars. We got hold of a rope at the light-ship, and the boat was capsized and turned bottom upwards. I got on the keel of the boat and took off my clothes, and then when the second boat came I jumped into the water and swam to the second boat. I got into her and then went up a hanging ladder that was over the quarter of the lightship. Brodie was on board the lightship before me. When we bore up, and before we took to the boats, the second mate told me to go to the carpenter and get the key of the sluice valves to let the water to the steam pump. I went to the carpenter, and he said that he had never received the key, and it could not be found. I soon after heard that the carpenter had been washed overboard. I saw the forehatch broken open, but I could not say whether it was by a sea shipped or the water in the hold.

By Mr. Forshaw: I did not try the choaks in the hawse pipes with the chains, but they were made, I am almost sure, to fit when the chains were not in the pipes.

By Mr. Raffles: The people on board were all sober as far as I know. Grog was served out twice to refresh the men but that was all.

By Captain Harris: I noticed her marks two days before she sailed, and the covering plank was then about three feet above the water. I am sure that the anchor did not pierce her bow when it was at the pipe, before it was catted.

By Captain Baker: I thought the weather was rather rough, but I did not think there was any danger on the morning that we sailed. I would call it a moderate gale. I considered the ship well fitted. One man failed to join the ship who had signed articles.

Other witnesses were examined and the court then adjourned.

[Lyman Danford Obey, a seaman, gave evidence that as to the fixing of the anchors. None of the anchors went through the bow of the vessel or through the deck.]

[Timothy O'Brien, engineer's store-keeper, said after the vessel bore up, the engineer ordered him to give a sledge hammer to the carpenter, and to tell him to knock a plate out at the bulwarks, so as to let the water off the ship. He gave the hammer to the carpenter, but he said he could do no good with it in consequence of the quantity of water on the deck.]

On Saturday, the enquiry into the circumstances attending the loss of the steamship *Lelia* was resumed before Mr. Raffles and Capts. Harris and Baker, nautical assessors, Mr. Hamel appearing as solicitor for the Board of Trade, and Mr. Forshaw for the owners of the ship.

James Forfar was called by Mr. Forshaw, and stated - I am the foreman shipwright for the Messrs. Miller. It is my duty to see that the small stores are in the ships built by Messrs. Miller, before they go to sea. I went on board the *Lelia* on Thursday previous to her sailing, by orders of the late Thomas Miller. I went first, because the mate nor any one on board did not know how the windlass worked, and I showed how it worked to the satisfaction of the mate. I saw the carpenter on board, and in consequence of his appearance, I saw the mate, and requested him to take charge of the small stores and deliver them to the carpenter. There were four plugs to the hawse pipes, there being only two hawse holes. There were two plugs for the hawse holes when the chains were bent and two holes[sic] when they were unbent, with an eye bolt through the centre of them. I delivered to the mate 22 galvanised crutches or rowlocks. That would be the proper number, and to spare, for the boats on board. I also delivered to the mate two keys for the sluice valves, and then two small keys to take the small cap off, and five keys for the padlocks of the hatches. On the trial trip I fitted the rowlocks myself in their places, and the oars, masts, and boathooks. That was on the 5th. The rudders were in the boats, but were not shipped. After the trial trip, the rowlocks were put into the carpenter's store-room in a bag, and I went on board on the Thursday before the ship sailed and re-delivered them to the mate.

Murtagh Byrne - I was employed to stow the *Lelia*. The principal part of the coal was on board when I went on the 7th January to the ship. The coal was stowed in the bunkers and in the fore and after hold. The bunkers were not then full, but were filled up afterwards. When I went on board the coals in the hold (about 120 tons) were stowed close up to the bulkhead of the bunkers, and I removed them amidships to make room [6 or 8 feet in each wing] for the cargo in the wings. I trimmed the ship, according to orders, six inches by the stern. I stowed the cargo in the wings up to the bulkheads, fore and aft. There were 40 tons of iron in the fore hold and the remainder was in the after hold, and there was a general cargo, mostly of hardware. The ship was not nearly full, either in the fore or after hold. [There was a vacant space before the cargo in the forehold between the cargo and the bulkhead of the forepeak]

Mr. Goold[Gould], surveyor of Customs, was sent for, and Mr. Raffles said that the court wished to have an explanation in ship's bill of contents, where it was stated that there were no passengers or troops.

Mr. Forshaw - I can explain that. She was not under the Passenger Act, and none of the gentlemen paid their passage.

Mr. Raffles - Yes, but under the 303rd section of the Act it is enacted "That the word passenger shall be held to mean any person carried in the steamship, other than the master and crew of such a vessel."

Mr. Forshaw - They were gentlemen who did not pay their passage, and therefore they were not called passengers.

Mr. Goold[Gould] said that the entry under the head of "passengers and troops" in the bill of contents was made on the authority of the captain of the ship. If Customs had been aware that there were passengers on board the ship would have required a Board of Trade certificate, without which she could not have cleared.

Mr. Forshaw - I do not think this is necessary for the purpose of this enquiry.

Mr. Raffles - We wanted to have an explanation of the entry. You contend that these people were not passengers because they had not paid for their passage.

Mr. Forshaw - I contend nothing, but I have an opinion about it myself.

There was some further conversation at the end of which Mr. Forshaw said - I do not deem it necessary in the interest of my clients to make any observations. I shall only confine myself to an expression of regret on their behalf, that on account of the perils of the sea, so many of their valued friends should have been lost by the loss of this ship. I presume that there will only be a report.

Mr. Raffles - Only a report, of course. We can give no judgement and will have no remark to make. The enquiry is now closed.

Notes on nautical terms:

The stem is the bow (fore, front, head) and the poop is at the stern (aft, back). The keel is the bottom. The forecastle is the sailor's accommodation space at the bow. A hurricane deck was a covering of the fore deck to protect it from waves.

The hull was made of overlapping plates of steel (called steaks here) with those nearest the keel being garboard, then bottom plates to the turn of the hull, then side plates with the sheer (called shear here) plates at the top of the side. The main deck stringer was horizontal and ran along the sides to support the deck.

The bulwark was the wall around the side of the deck with holes in it (scuppers) and hinged flaps (wash ports), the top of the bulwark is the gunwale. Covering board means main deck. A scuttle was a flush hole in the deck itself, covered with a plate. A hatch is a larger opening in the deck. A hawse pipe is the pipe by which the anchor chain goes from the foredeck to the outside of the hull. A choke (choak here) was used to block this pipe and stop water coming up it. An anchor catted was lifted up.

Bulkheads are vertical walls separating different compartments in the hull.

Bunkers are for storing coal. Holds for storing cargo.

Sluice valves are to connect pipes to pumps.

Kelsons are heavy supports - usually for the engine.

The stoke-hold (stoke-hole) is the area of the engine where coal is fed to the boilers by the firemen.

Sponsons are the projections forward and aft of the paddles.

Life boats were lowered from davits by means of a tackle (ropes).

The quarter boat would be stowed aft, the waist boat further forward.

The oars were held in place either by two vertical rods (thoul pins here) or a metal rowlock (rollock, crutch). Thwarts are cross pieces in a boat.

Broached means turned across the waves.

A point means 11.25 degrees.

Board of Trade Report

I have the honour to report for the information of your Lordships that I have in conjunction with Captains Harris and Baker as Nautical Assessors held an Enquiry into the loss of the steamship *Lelia* which foundered off the port of Liverpool on the 14th of this month.

The *Lelia* was a paddle-wheel steamer built of steel by Messrs. W C Miller and Sons of Liverpool in 1864 of the burthen of 640 tons gross and 431 tons registered. She was schooner rigged and clincher built with one deck and a half raised poop. She had engines of 300 horse power. Her length was 252 feet her breadth was 30 feet and her depth 12 6/10 feet. She was owned as appears from her certificate of registry by Henry Elias Moss of Liverpool broker.

The *Lelia* left Liverpool at 9.30 am on the 14th of this month under the command of Mr Thomas Buxton Skinner who held a certificate of competency as Master and a Crew of 49 all told, as appears by the ships articles. She had also on board two pilots, one named Williams belonging to Liverpool, and the other whose name did not appear belonging to Cork, six passengers for Bermuda, viz. Captain Sinclair, Mr Cuddy, Mr C L Hobson, Mr J B Cropper, Mr Gerchart, and Mr Campbell, and Mr Thomas Miller of the builders firm and

Mr J Clarke who were to return with the Liverpool pilot from Holyhead. Her cargo consisted of 40 tons of iron and 45 tons of general cargo, and she carried 460 tons of coals in the bunkers and holds. There was no deck load. Her draft of water as nearly as could be ascertained was from 10 feet to 10 feet 4 inches aft. Her draft forward does not seem to have been noticed. At the time the *Lelia* proceeded to sea, the barometer was very low: the reading at the observatory being at 8.30 am 28.34, but from that hour it began to rise. According to the same authority, the wind at 9 am was SSW moderate increasing gradually up to 11 am when it blew a fresh gale from the westward, which attained its height at 5.15 pm when the anemometer shewed a pressure of 21 lbs on the square foot. There was no Fitzroy signal hoisted on the 14th.

After passing the Crosby light ship, the wind and sea began to rise, but the *Lelia* did not ship any water of consequence until she had passed the Bell Buoy which she did at noon. About 1 pm some heavy seas were shipped which started the guard rail on the bridge. At this time the vessel was slowed to get the port anchor in board which had been lifted on the rail, clear of the water, in leaving the river, but it would seem that after the anchors had been stowed, the covers of the space in the hurricane deck which admitted the anchors on board were not put on and shortly afterwards, when they set on full speed, the sea rushed through these openings carrying away the fore bulkhead of the deck house, gutting the interior and washing the mens' berths and bedding over the fore part of the deck. The man-hole scuttle leading to the fore peak was also washed off, and the fore compartment became filled with water and thus brought the ship down by the head, while the fore part of the deck was also filled with water as far as the main shaft of the engines. It was impossible to get sufficiently forward to see what was the matter, on account of the water and the sea breaking over her, the carpenter having failed to knock out a plate in her bulwarks to let out the water. The foremost pumps were at once rigged and set to work to no purpose; the men being washed from them. At this juncture the pilot Williams, after speaking to the men at the wheel, who expressed an opinion that the vessel was settling down by the head, consulted with Captain Skinner, during which time the engines were slowed and she went much more easily, so that pilot thought she might reach Holyhead. A heavy sea was now shipped which shook the vessel all over. The Captain decided to return to Liverpool and, with considerable difficulty, she was got before the wind, then blowing WNW, being at this time abreast of the Great Ormes head.

She was then put on full speed, but the sea continued to break over her, and she steered very wildly from being so much by the head. After standing back for about an hour and a quarter, another heavy sea struck her on the port quarter, broaching her to, with her head to the northward, and she lay helpless in the trough of the sea for ten or fifteen minutes. With great difficulty they again succeeded in getting her before the wind. Abreast of the north west lightship, distant 3 or 4 miles, an hour later, she again broached to and became unmanageable, rolled heavily, shipping a large body of water which burst open the fore hatches apparently from below. At this time the covering board forward was level with the water and the Captain now ordered the boats to be got out.

The starboard waist boat was first lowered and the two pilots, some of the passengers, and several of the crew, from 14 to 16 persons in all, got into her. But as she was never seen to leave the ship, it is probable that she was cut down by the sponson beam. Captain Skinner who had been in this boat and superintended the placing of the people in her, returned on board and ordered the port waist boat to be lowered which was done and she got away safely with twelve persons viz, ten firemen, one seaman and the second steward James Tinker. The port quarter boat was then lowered and two able seamen named Brody and Curry, who up to this time had remained at the wheel, were ordered by Captain Skinner to take to the boats, saying that he would follow. Brody succeeded in getting into the boat which shoved off with 18 persons, leaving the Captain and Curry on deck. On rounding the stern of the steamer, the Captain and Curry were seen hanging on the after tackles of the starboard quarter boat which was down and full of water, but being then nearly dark, they were unable to see what had become of the people who had been in her. The port lifeboat made for the North West lightship as best they could, for, having found no rowlocks in the boat, they were compelled to make tholepins out of the boathook staff. Their rudder also was washed away, not having been properly secured by a lanyard. This boat and the port waist boat reached the light ship about the same time, but unfortunately the former was capsized. Every assistance was rendered by the small staff at the light ship and eventually twelve persons were saved with great difficulty and gained the lightship. The remaining eighteen, among whom was Mr Thomas Miller, lamentably perished when their safety seemed almost on the point of being secured.

I must not omit to mention that, when the *Lelia* bore up for Liverpool, the ensign was hoisted Union down, as a signal of distress to a steamer, since ascertained to have been the *Sovereign* which had left the Mersey for Bristol on the same morning. The steamer followed the *Lelia* for some time but, as the latter did not slow her engines, and the *Sovereign* was unable to overtake her, she proceeded on her voyage. It is possible, perhaps probable, that had the engines of the *Lelia* been slowed and a communication effected with the *Sovereign* that all hands might have been saved.

Such is the sad story of the loss of the *Lelia* so far as it could be gathered from the narration of the few survivors who were brought before the Court. Forty seven lives were lost, among whom were the Captain, and all the Certificated Officers of this ill-fated vessel. The Court has therefore no judgement to pronounce and can only call attention to certain facts which were elicited in evidence.

The engines were manufactured by Messrs Fawcett Preston and Company of Liverpool. From the evidence of Mr H T Sillem, a partner in that firm, it would appear that they were of 300 horse power; her boilers were loaded at 30 pounds on the square inch, and that, on her trial trip on the 5th of this month, she worked up to 6 1/2 times more than her nominal power. With this enormous steam power in a vessel of her slight construction and tonnage, when driven against a north westerly gale in a heavy sea, it cannot be a matter of surprise that she made very bad weather of it. Coupling this state of facts with the omission to close the anchor hatches and hawse-holes, by which the forepeak became filled, there appears to be ample reason to account for the subsequent disaster.

It does not appear to the Court that the ship was overloaded. According to the evidence of Mr Edwin Miller, the ship could be safely loaded to 10 feet 6 inches which she certainly did not exceed. But, however, this might be in smooth water and with fair weather. It must be questionable whether a vessel of her size and construction is adapted for carrying a heavy cargo in a sea such as she experienced.

I enquired carefully, as will be seen by a reference to the evidence into the state of the weather on the morning when the *Lelia* sailed, and it would certainly not appear to have been such, at the hour of her departure, as to have given intimation of the violent gale which subsequently and speedily came on. On the contrary, the barometer had begun to rise. A Fitzroy signal had indeed been hoisted on the 12th but, as I have already observed, there was none up on the 14th. Still considering the character of the vessel, I cannot but think that it would have been prudent to have delayed her departure, for only three other vessels, all of which were much more strongly built, ventured to sea on that morning. It was not however insinuated before the Court that any pressure was put upon the Captain by the owners or any other persons to induce him to go to sea.

I am bound to comment upon the equipment of the boats, four in number. It would seem that the builders had already delivered on board the necessary equipments into the care of the mate, but, owing to culpable negligence in some quarter, the boats, when required for use, were found to be without rowlocks, thus rendering them unmanageable when they reached the lightship and contributing materially to the loss of life. A similar neglect occurred in reference to the key of the sluice valves, although on board, it could not be found when required to let the water from the fore compartment to the engine pumps.

One other circumstance remains to noticed. By the Custom House clearance papers it would appear that no passengers were declared to be on board, whereas there were six passengers, in addition to the two gentlemen who purposed to leave the ship with the pilot. The *Lelia* therefore obtained her port clearance without the usual surveyor's certificate necessary for a ship carrying passengers.

It becomes a question for the consideration of your Lordships whether the omission to procure the proper certificate is not in violation of the 303rd and 318th sections of the Merchant Shipping Act 1854.

TS Raffles Police Magistrate Liverpool 30 January 1865

Liverpool-built Blockade Runners

Shipyards in Liverpool (Jones Quiggin, WC Miller & Sons and WH Potter) and on the other side of the Mersey in Birkenhead (Laird Bros.) and Seacombe (Bowdler Chaffer) built blockade runners. Vessels for use of the Confederate Navy were also built by Millers and Lairds. Mersey shipyards were responsible for repairing blockade runners (such as *Georgia* and *Gibraltar*, both ex CSN-vessels) and completing blockade runners that had been launched elsewhere, such as *Let her Rip/Wando* from the Clyde and *Agnes Louisa/Grapeshot* from Jarrow. In the early years of blockade running, locally built paddle steamers were converted into blockade runners. One conversion, *Denbigh* (built in 1860 by Lairds as an iron paddle steamer for North Wales excursion trips, 182,22,8.7, 250gt), had a trial in the Mersey on 23 August 1863, and was very successful, running 26 times through the blockade to Gulf ports from 10 January 1864, before being lost on 23 May 1865. Her wreck has been located and is explored by divers.

Here I list the blockade runners built, as such, on the Mersey. They are listed in date order of their registration. The size is given in feet (length, breadth, depth), the tonnage as gross (gt), register (rt) or burden (bt), and the engine power is nominal horse power. Since many of these ships were built partly of iron and partly of steel, the register entries describing the material of construction appear rather unreliable.

Registered at Liverpool in 1863:

Banshee,   registered 14 February, ran 14 times from 13
May, captured 21 November. Built Jones
Quiggin, steel paddle steamer 120hp, 214,20,8,
325gt, 217rt, 533bt. Owned John Lawrence for
the Anglo Trading Co. Ran under Captain
Jonathon Steele.

Phantom,   registered 21 May, ran 4 times from 15 July, lost
23 September. Built William C Miller & Son,
steel screw steamship, engines Fawcett &
Preston 170hp, 192.9,22,12.2, 322gt, 266rt.
Delivered from Liverpool by Capt. Tessier. Ran
under Capt. S. G. Porter. Owned William
Thompson Mann of Liverpool for Fraser
Trentholm, bought by the Confederate
Ordnance Bureau July 63.

Lucy,   registered 15 October, ran 21 times from 21
November, captured 3 November 1864. Built
Jones Quiggin, iron paddle steamer, engines
Fawcett's 140hp, 215,20,10.75, 300gt. Capt. J.
A. Duguid until 26-6-64 at Nassau then Captain
John Beaton. Owned Edward James Lomnitz of
Liverpool for Fraser Trentholm.

Wild Dayrell,   registered 12 November, ran 4 times from 5
January 1864, lost 1 February 1864. Built Jones
Quiggin, iron paddle steamer 140hp, 215,
20,10.75, 320gt. Delivered Capt. T. Cubbins.

Owned Edward Lawrence of Liverpool for the
Anglo Confederate Trading Co.

Registered at Liverpool in 1864:

Mary,   registered 27 January, ran 7 times in Gulf from
March 1864, eventually trapped in Mobile.
Built Lairds, iron paddle steamer, 120hp,
198,30, 9.3, 389gt, 279rt. Ran under Captain
Pete. Owned Arthur Forwood for Leech,
Harrison & Forwood.

Let her B,   registered 26 March, trial 23 March, ran 14
times from 30 May, renamed Chicora, survived.
Built WC Miller (subcontract from Jones
Quiggin), iron paddle steamer, engines
Fawcett's 180hp, 221, 26, 10, 365gt, 930bt.
Delivered Capt. James Raison, ran under Capt.
H. Holgate. Owned Chicora Importing
Exporting Co.

Badger,   trial 19 & 23 March, ran once 31 May, lost 10
September. Built Jones Quiggin, iron paddle
steamer 150hp, 218,24.3,11.6, 375gt, 623bt.
Delivered Capt. Henry Wilson Priestly. Owned
Josiah Jones for Fraser Trentholm.

Lynx,   registered 6 April, ran 9 times from 28 May, lost
25 September. Built Jones Quiggin, steel paddle
steamer, 150hp, 218,24,11.5, 372gt, 233rt.

Delivered and ran under Capt. Edward C. Reid.
Owned Richard Wright for Fraser Trentholm.

Fox, registered 22 April, ran 18 times from 8 June,
survived. Built Jones Quiggin, iron paddle steamer,
120hp, 219,22,10.2, 325gt, 230rt. Delivered Capt.
William Raisbeck, ran under Capt. Simpson
Adkins. Owned Josiah Jones for Fraser Trentholm.

Mary Celestia, registered at London 25 April, ran 8 times from
27 May, sank 26 September. Built William C.
Miller & Son, iron paddle steamer, engines
Fawcett & Preston 140hp, 221,22.1,10.4, 314gt,
207rt. Ran under Captain Michael Ursina then
Commander Arthur Sinclair. Owned James
Cameron for Crenshaw & Co.

Hope, registered 7 July, launched 25 Nov 1863, ran
twice from 27 August 1864, captured 22
October. Built Jones Quiggin, steel paddle
steamer, engines Jack & Co, Victoria Foundry,
350hp, 281,35,15, 1046 gt. Delivered Capt.
William Bell, ran under Capt. Hammer. Owned
William Quiggin for Fraser Trenholm.

Owl, registered 25 July, launched 21 June 1864, ran 4
times from 24 August, survived. Built Jones
Quiggin, steel paddle steamer, engines Lairds
180hp, 230,26,10.5, 466gt, 330rt. Owned
William Quiggin for Fraser Trentholm, then to
Confederacy December 1864. Delivery Capt.

Mathew Butcher, ran under Lieutenant
Donnington, then Commander John Maffitt, CSN.

Bat,   registered 18 August, launched 21 June 1864,
captured 8 October 1864 on first run. Built
Jones Quiggin steel paddle steamer, engines
from Watt & Co. of London 180hp, 230,26,9.5,
466gt, 770 bt. Ran under Captain A. Hora.
Owned William Quiggin for Fraser Trenholm,
intended to Confederacy.

Colonel Lamb,   registered 16 September, launched 25 May,
trial 13 October, ran twice from 29 November,
survived. Built Jones Quiggin , steel paddle
steamer 350hp, 279,36,15.5, 1132gt, 800rt,
1788bt. Captain Thomas J Lockwood. Owned
William Quiggin for Fraser Trenholm, intended
to Confederacy.

Stag,   registered 19 October, launched 8 August, trial
15 October, ran twice from 4 December,
captured 19 January 1865. Built Bowdler
Chaffer (subcontract from Jones Quiggin), steel
paddle steamer, engines Messrs Stephenson of
Newcastle on Tyne 180hp, 230,26,12, 465gt,
299rt. Delivered Capt. William Pinchon. Owned
Josiah Jones for Fraser Trentholm, for
Confederacy.

Deer,   registered 12 November, captured 18 February
1865 on first run. Built WH Potter (subcontract

from Jones Quiggin) iron & steel paddle
steamer 180hp, 230,26.2,10.5, 465gt, 330rt,
857bt. Delivered Capt. James B Butler. Owned
Richard Philips for Fraser Trentholm, for
Confederacy.

Secret,   registered 18 November, launched about 22
August, arrived Nassau 19 Jan 1865, did not
run. Built Bowdler Chaffer (subcontract from
Jones Quiggin), steel paddle steamer 180hp,
232,26,11, 467gt, 800bt. Delivered Capt.
Richard Brickby. Owned John Newton Beech.

Dream,   registered 3 December, arrived Nassau Jan
1865, did not run. Built WH Potter (subcontract
from Jones Quiggin) steel paddle steamer
180hp, 231,26,11.2, 466gt, 296rt, 800bt.
Ordered Fraser Trenholm, then sold to Beech,
Root & Co.

Lark,   registered 3 December, ran 8 times in Gulf from
20 January 1865, survived. Built Lairds, steel
paddle steamer 120hp, 210,23,10, 388gt, 267rt,
800bt. Delivered Capt. Thomas Griffiths.
Owned John Laird for Fraser Trentholm.

Georgia Belle,   registered 16 December, launched 1 Oct, left
Liverpool but did not run. Built Jones Quiggin,
iron & steel paddle steamer, engines James Watt
220hp, 250,28,10.9, 972gt, 452rt.

Wren,	registered 24 December, ran 6 times in Gulf from 7 February 1865, crew took her to Key West June 1865. Built Lairds, steel paddle steamer 120hp, 211,23,10, 389gt, 296rt, 800bt. Owned John Laird for Fraser Trentholm.

Registered at Liverpool in 1865 (none ran blockade):

Lelia,	trial 5 January, registered 11 January, lost 14 January. Built WC Miller, steel paddle steamer, engines Fawcett's, 300hp, 252,30,12.6, 640gt, 430rt, 1100bt. Owned Henry Elias Moss for Crenshaws.
Widgeon and **Snipe,**	launched 25 February 1865. Built Jones Quiggin, steel paddle steamers, engines G. Forrester, Vauxhall Foundry 180hp, 225,24,11, 409gt, 645 bt. Ordered J. K. Gilliat for the Confederacy.
Abigail,	registered 17 March 1865, launched 15 October 1864. Built WC Miller, steel paddle steamer, engines James Watt, 300hp, 250,30,13, 644gt, 1100bt. Owned WC Miller (ordered Fraser Trentholm)
Ray,	registered 17 March 1865. Built WC Miller, steel paddle steamer, engines James Watt, 300hp, 252,29,12.5, 644gt, 430rt, 1100bt. Owned WC Miller (ordered Fraser Trentholm)

Rosine,	launched 15 October. Built Jones Quiggin, steel paddle steamer, engines James Watt 300hp 270,33,15, 900gt, 500rt, 1391bt. Ordered J. K. Gilliat for the Confederacy.
Hornet,	launched 15 December. Built Jones Quiggin, steel paddle steamer, 250,28,10.9, 573gt, 290rt, 770bt. Ordered Charles Prioleau for Fraser Trentholm.
Ruby,	Built Jones Quiggin, steel paddle steamer, 261.1,33,15.6, 900gt, 500rt, 1391bt. Ordered J. K. Gilliat for the Confederacy.
Plover and *Curlew,*	launched 25 February 1865. Built Jones Quiggin, steel paddle steamers, engines James Watt 180hp, 225,24,11, 409gt, 645bt. Ordered J. K. Gilliat for the Confederacy.
Penguin,	Built Lairds, steel paddle steamer, 240,30,13.2, 659gt, 1063bt. Ordered Fraser Trentholm for the Confederacy.
Swan,	Built Bowdler Chaffer (subcontract from Jones Quiggin), steel paddle steamer, 216,26,10.9, 470gt, 296rt.
Albatross,	similar to Penguin but not registered.

Wasp, not registered. Ordered from Jones Quiggin, steel paddle steamer, 250,28,10.75, 280rt, 800 bt.

Some additional, incomplete, information.

John Robinson built several ships at his yard near Dukes Dock in Liverpool for the Dixie Line (owners Robinson, Philpott and Broadbent). The *Richmond* was built December 1862 (100,22.6,12.2, 164rt), the *Virginia* (117.5,23.2,11.6, 231bt) was launched on 10 July 1863, the *Jeff Davies* (144,23.6,12.2, 237.rt) was built in September 1863. They were Liverpool registered wooden barques of an usual construction, patented by Robinson, with 3 keels, a flat bottom and only straight timbers needed in their construction. This suggests that they were designed to visit unfrequented parts of the Confederacy, taking the ground to load and unload. There is no record of them running the blockade and all three survived.

Bagdad Packet, registered 29 January 1864. Built at Liverpool, iron paddle steamer, engines 60hp, 124.6,22,6.1, 130gt, 106rt. Owned Edward McDowell. Three different captains assigned up to 5 October 1864. Vessel cleared Liverpool for Matamoros and was re-registered at Galveston Texas in January 1866. Bagdad was the name of a beach at Matamoros in Mexico, just across the Rio Grande from Texas, which was used by ships to import/export to the confederacy via Mexico, so avoiding the blockade.

Lelia

ßibliography

Liverpool Daily Post, Echo, Mercury and Courier.
Liverpool Telegraph and Daily Shipping and Commercial Gazette
Illustrated London News
Times
Fleetwood Chronicle.
Bermuda Royal Gazette.
Gore's Directory of Liverpool
Liverpool Shipwreck and Humane Society, Annual Reports.
Mersey Docks and Harbour Board Records, Merseyside Maritime
Museum.
Shipwrecks of North Wales, Ivor Wynne Jones, 1973.
Wrecks of Liverpool Bay, C. Michael, 1994.
Wrecks and Casualties 1859, Board of Trade report.
Britain's First Lifeboat Station at Formby, Merseyside 1776-1918,
Barbara and Reginald Yorke, 1982.
The Story of the Hoylake and West Kirby Lifeboats, Jeff Morris
1993.
The Story of the New Brighton Lifeboats, Jeff Morris, 1986.
The History of the Point of Ayr Lifeboats, Jeff Morris, 1998
Wreck and Rescue on the Coast of Wales, Vol. 2, The Story of the
North Wales Lifeboats, Henry Parry, 1973.

Shipbuilding, Theoretical and Practical, I. Watts et al., ed. W. J. M. Rankine, 1866.

Modern Marine Engineering Illustrated, N. P. Burgh, 1867.

The Secret Service of the Confederate States in Europe, James D. Bulloch, vol I and II, 1883.

Confederate Commerce-Destroyers. The eventful cruise of the Florida: G. Terry Sinclair(jr), Century Magazine, 1898.

Two years on the Alabama, Arthur Sinclair(jr), 1896.

Memoirs of Service Afloat, Admiral Raphael Semmes, 1868.

Lifeline of the Confederacy, Stephen R Wise, 1988

Fossets, Horace White, 1958.

Running the Blockade, Thomas E. Taylor, 1896.

Blockade Running during the Civil War, Francis B. C. Bradlee, 1925.

Masters of the Shoals, Tales of Cape Fear pilots who ran the Union Blockade, Jim McNeil, 2003.

Ghost Ships of the Mersey, K. J. Williams.

The Loss of the Lelia, Confederate Veteran, S. Brown.

Civil War Naval Chronology, 1861-65, Navy History Division, Navy Dept., 1971.

Official Records of the Union and Confederate Navies in the War of Rebellion.

R. Bolling Batte records, Library of Virginia.

Dictionary of American Fighting Ships.

www.history.navy.mil

www.civilwarhome.com; www.csnavy.org

www.csa-dixie.com/Liverpool_Dixie

cdl.library.cornell.edu/cgi-bin/moa